PULSE

A Paramedic's Walk Along the Lines of Life and Death

JAMES PACE

J. K. PACE

Cover design by Deranged Doctor Design

Paramedic photograph by Shillawna Ruffner

ISBN 978-1-957936-01-7

To our kids

Thank you to *Puerto del Sol*, in which the essay, "Wreck,"
was originally published.

Disclaimer

First things first.

Names are changed.

Places too.

A lot of identifying details as well.

If you think we're talking about you, we're probably not. Unless you're Brad—and then we definitely are.

SECOND THINGS SECOND.

This collection of essays was a collaboration between James (paramedic) and Jean (writer). Most of the stories belong to James, though at times Jean will chime in with a viewpoint that is all her own. At times (many times) their voices may merge into something that isn't quite either of them—James's experiences given voice through Jean. If you talk to James, he won't spout off a thousand words about an experience (three sentences is more his style). If you talk to Jean, she won't know what an electrocardio-

1

graph is or how it works. If you talked to both, you'll get something more like this collection of essays.

THIRD THINGS THIRD.

Some of these essays might hurt to read. It hurt to write some of them too. That's because this is a collection of true experiences told as honestly as possible. Which means that sometimes people weren't perfectly nice; sometimes things didn't go perfectly well; sometimes (lots of times) people died. Please consider this your trigger warning. Some of these essays deal with intense situations that include trauma, death, murder, suicide, miscarriage, guns, and abuse. Because this is a book about a job that deals with these issues. (Though it's not all gloom—sometimes people live; sometimes they even laugh!)

We hope you enjoy reading it as much as we have enjoyed creating it. We hope it changes a little piece of you as it has changed a big piece of us.

And, remember: walk, don't run.

Introduction

I got into Emergency Medical Services (EMS) because I was twenty-four years old and wanted to do something exciting. I wanted to help people too. And I thought those two things—excitement and helping people—would exist hand in hand. With a little sprinkle of glory thrown in for good measure.

I started out as an EMT (Emergency Medical Technician) and after a couple years went back to school to become a paramedic. If you don't know what this means because you never realized there was a difference between an EMT and a paramedic, join the club. An EMT is a basic technician. They can put patients on oxygen, assist with medications that the patient already has, use splints, and do CPR. A paramedic can give more advanced care (though what is legal varies from state to state). A paramedic can intubate, start IVs, administer breathing treatments, give narcotics as well as cardiac medications, and take care of serious trauma through more advanced means. For example, we can decompress a chest (stick a needle in a chest to let excess air out) or start an IO (stick a needle in a bone, usually because we can't get an IV and a patient really needs a medication quickly).

But I'm getting ahead of myself.

My first call, as a newly minted EMT—ready for excitement and glory and helping people—was to evaluate a guy who was in police custody. We got vitals (blood pressure, pulse, respirations, oxygen levels) and he refused transport. After that I think he went to jail.

No big thrills, no great boost to humanity.

This first call was followed by a series of lift assists (just like it sounds—help an old person get up) and transports (also just what it sounds like—take a person from one hospital to another). At this point, my "exciting" job was shaping up to be little more than a taxicab with a red light on top. As for helping people—I guess I was doing that, but not in a way that seemed to need any type of qualified technician, and not in a way that was going to win me that badge of glory any time soon.

In fact, I quickly learned that we got a lot more calls from people who needed help going to the bathroom than people who needed help not dying.

I've been called to help a patient get her leg back in the bed—that's right—her leg was dangling out and she needed someone to lift it into the bed. So she called 911. I've gotten called to help untangle an extension cord from an elderly man's wheelchair. I've been called to rub lotion on someone's back rash. I've been called to help a man take off his pants so he could go to bed. I've been called to retrieve remote controls. And, on more than one occasion, I've been asked to fill up a soda, maybe get a bag of chips, so the patient didn't have to get out of bed.

Soda pop refills are not particularly exciting. Or fulfilling.

But our calls didn't end with the absurd or mundane.

I also remember my first "exciting" call. The lights. The sirens. A cardiac arrest.

She died.

Not very climactic, is it? No enormous contribution to society. No cause for glory there either.

At the end of the call, my more experienced partner leaned over and muttered, "That didn't go well."

I would soon learn that many things in EMS didn't go well.

Rollovers, shootings, stabbings, beatings, murders, suicides, car accidents. And even once, a mass shooting at a business. The nature of this job is that things not be going well at the start. You hope, you try, to change that, but it doesn't always work.

So, sure, mingled in with all the dull and sometimes irritating calls, I got my excitement—a whole lifetime's worth.

It came with a bit of a cost. You'll read about some of that in this book. I should warn you that many of these essays might make you sad. They make me sad too. However, somewhere under that sadness, I did find a little bit of what I was looking for. Maybe not the glory (we all know the firefighters win that one), and—after twenty-three years in EMS, twenty-one on the ground and two in a helicopter—I'm long past the thrill. But some nights, even now, I find scraps of humanity—beautiful pieces in the broken-up mosaic of our world.

We're the ones who walk into your house, into your emergency, into your life that will never be the same.

When we walk out, we're never quite the same either.

PART I

Houses of Sorrow

There's Things I Remember

The call my wife most remembers is one that has grown hazy in my mind.

"The murder-suicide. Don't you remember?" she asks.

Misty lines of detail return. The woman lying in the hall. The man in the kitchen, gun in his lap. Both of them young. Gunshots to the head. Not much blood on the floor, which was unusual. Long enough dead that their bodies had begun purpling at the base where the blood, no longer pumping, had begun to pool.

We would not transport patients that day. We bent over gray faces, checked their unmoving hearts for electrical impulses, stepped back as though they were gray mannequins left crumpled after a Halloween dance.

The neighbors had called. I think. Or maybe a family member. A report of arguing turned to shots, turned to silence. A Lifetime movie plot. Dead at my feet.

"And the dad," my wife prods, tugging at my memory. "That was the saddest part."

And it was. The living always are. But until that

moment, my mind had erased him. An older man. Sitting on the steps as we had entered the apartment building.

Sobbing.

Father or stepfather to the woman. Possibly the one who found them, possibly notified by the police. We don't know. We don't ask questions, not that type anyway, when we enter a scene. We look for danger; we look for signs of patient life.

Finding none, it falls to the police to ask more questions, write reports, look for logic or sense where none could possibly be found.

Us? We leave. Pack up our monitors, fill out our paperwork, snap off our gloves. Turn our backs to the bodies and exit the scene. Out the door, down the sidewalk, past the sobbing father. Only this time, we stop. My partner reaches out, puts an arm around the father.

And then we are gone. Another call comes, then another after that. An old woman who fell going to the bathroom, a man who vomited from a stomach bug. A stream of needs and sirens and scenes. Until morning comes and I go home. Tell my wife about the night. Still fresh. With pieces that hurt.

"I can't believe you barely remember it," she says to me now. "You were really bothered by it then."

This is true. Of course. Two lives left gray and purple from a moment's fury. Two children who remain behind, probably hers and not his.

"You looked them up on Facebook," she reminds me. And I remember that as well, the pictures from her feed coming back into my mind. So I must have cared, must have hurt, must have sought them out. It sounds creepy—maybe it is—but most of us do it. Public information we reach for in hopes of finding . . . what? Humanity to connect to the tragedy? Pieces now lost to a puzzle that can't be fixed? Whatever it is we're looking for, I doubt most of us find it.

Me? I discovered a man who liked guns, wedding photos less than half a decade old, pictures of a couple of kids. And a pretty young woman. Her face—so different from the one I had encountered.

In life, she was attractive, vibrant, hugging, smiling. In death, she was . . . dead. A word that erases—beauty, youth, color, style, charm, money, love, hate. Death equalizes. And death forgets.

Apparently I do too.

What can I say? Too many shards from too many nights. What I most remember now is a call from a few days ago. A suicidal man. Standing in the alley behind his house, gun in hand. The police trying to talk him down, get the weapon, save a life.

We waited—"staging," they call it. As though we are ready in the wings for our next big cue. We are.

Minutes climbing into hours. One squad car multiplying into many. Talking, reasoning, pleading. Desperate, the police shoot him with bean bags, a method of getting a person to drop a gun. It doesn't work. He holds it. He shoots.

Our cue.

We enter the scene. The man is dead—shot to the head, but his heart doesn't know it yet. He takes a breath.

We work him, knowing he will die.

Later, at the hospital, his niece arrives. The family knew he was depressed, struggling. Now they know he will probably not live. But still, as families do, they hope. I'm cleaning the ambulance. The niece approaches. "I know you can't tell me much, but can you say anything?"

Just as I cannot give life where none remains, I cannot

grant hope when there is so little. "He has a heartbeat, but it's not promising."

And knowing it's true, she cries.

I choke now, telling this story, remembering it, watching her hope crumple.

Though in a year, maybe even a few weeks, the memory will dim—this patient, his niece. Others will push in to take their places as others always do. Some I'll remember, but most I'll forget.

Casualty, Massive

J.K. Pace

When James comes home in the morning, I roll toward him, ask the same question I ask every day, "How was your night?"

"There was a mass shooting." Five simple words. Unreal. He works in a rural community in the south.

But whether anyone wants to believe it or not, it is real. Yahoo news says so, the TV anchors, the radio. When your family moves to a small community for your husband to work as a paramedic, you don't expect a mass shooting. Ever. And yet one has occurred.

He cannot calm down in the morning, relax into sleep. I take the kids to my meeting, visit a friend. He finally falls asleep.

In the afternoon, it's harder. He cannot stop thinking about it: the pictures and words won't leave his mind. Another body every few paces down the hall, hearts quivering in desperate electrical pulses that will never bring them back. I sit beside him, stroke his hand, hold his waist, try to ask the right questions and say the right things.

I notice blood on his watch. He takes it off, washes it.

Later I will do the laundry—a special batch for his uniform—the crusted blood of people who have died.

I was not there, cannot imagine it. Still, it hurts me to see him, to think of the families in their shock and suffering. I feel guilty too—for my healthy family, my small happinesses, the meals and trips to the store, the boring details of my life.

And here the story suffers from a gap—one I try to suffuse with some type of meaning, some moral, a life theme perhaps. Nothing fits. Nothing fills. Each one empty or preachy or half-lived. I delete, re-read, re-try. Still, the space sits blank. And there, I guess I find my theme.

James goes back to work the next day, a fact that seems impossible, but isn't. Everyone on his shift does it. And the day after that.

Through the gaps, the spaces that can't be filled. They return.

Day to day.

Person to person.

Life to life.

At the Table of Strangers

We enter crack houses and foster houses, group homes and strip clubs, trailers, mansions, split levels, ramblers, ramshackles, bungalows, old houses, new houses, brick, vinyl, aluminum, wood. We enter bars, temples, bowling alleys, churches, skating rinks, doctor's offices, jails, barges, fields, factories, stores, gas stations, laundromats, cars, woods, bushes, Walmart, Target, Dillard's. Buses, apartments, malls, schools, studios.

Tonight, we enter the country—a thirteen-minute drive. A call for someone not breathing. Dispatch informs us that CPR has been started. Usually a call like this takes us to a nursing home, maybe an apartment or a stone house with a wheelchair ramp leading right to the door. And usually at the other end of these calls, we find a dead person.

Even before we arrive, dispatch radios, "CPR stopped." Normal enough. Probably an old person, maybe a heart patient or an ancient asthmatic. Now they're dead.

But death—so perfectly reliable, so strikingly typical— she holds a few cruel cards up her sleeve.

We enter a nice country home, greeted by a sobbing thirty-something woman. A wife. She takes us to the patient. Forty years old. Not excessively heavy, no history of heart trouble, no asthma, no indication the night before that he would be anything but awake in the morning.

We walk in just as the woman's parents arrive, accompanied by a girl—our dead patient's daughter. She had been staying the night with her grandparents. The girl looks about ten—the same age as one of my daughters. She has been crying.

The sheriff is also there, along with a volunteer firefighter. The sheriff knows someone in the neighborhood and on his drive, he watched each house, hoping that the one he stopped at wouldn't be his friend's. It wasn't, and he is relieved—a fact he expresses a little loudly in front of the family.

"A crazy night," the firefighter concurs. True enough, but through the talk and explanations that ensue among us, I know the little girl is in the other room with her grandparents. The sheriff's relief about his friend is this family's disaster; our crazy night is their life that will never be the same.

I've already hooked the patient up to the EKG (electrocardiogram) although it's not really necessary. The patient's skin is cool, his blood pooling violet at his back. But it helps to have the EKG—the flat line, the lack of electrical impulses in the heart, the picture that is worth a thousand words. The EKG brings a closure that sentences can't. It gives me something to chart, and a science to the dialogue that inevitably follows.

"I'm sorry," I tell the new widow. "There's nothing we can do."

Sometimes people beg, hoping we're the type powerful enough to raise the lost from the dead.

But she knows. She knew when she stopped CPR, knew when she dressed him in his pajamas so he wouldn't be lying around in his underwear when we arrived—her embarrassment the privilege and curse of the living.

What no one knows is *why*—a question that haunts the young families that sometimes remain.

In place of begging for a miracle, she falls into replaying, reliving, rethinking what might have been.

He had sleep apnea. He snored. She'd left the room to sleep somewhere else. It wasn't unusual; she'd done it hundreds of times before. But what if she had stayed with him, heard the breathing stop, awoken or revived him immediately? What if she'd gotten up to go to the bathroom, noticed him sooner, heard him struggling to breathe? What if he'd had a better pillow, lost a little weight, not eaten so much before bedtime? What if, what if, what if, what if. It's a list that could go forever, and it hurts to hear it.

"There's nothing you could have done," I tell her.

All this time, the daughter sniffles from the living room where she sits with her grandparents, crying over the dead dad who's younger than I am. I have to walk into the kitchen so I don't hear it, so I don't start crying too. It is not my job to sob with strangers.

The sheriff and firefighter finish any business they have and leave. The house quiets. We stay to wait for the coroner.

Forty-five minutes to sit in a kitchen that isn't our own. Forty-five minutes to linger at the table of someone else's darkest hour. Forty-five minutes to be strangers where strangers don't belong. They talk about religious services, whether they should have their preacher come out for a last rite of some sort. They discuss money and estate, siblings and family, phone calls that will have to be made.

Each item on the shell-shocked to-do punctuated with another idea of something they could have done, should have changed, could have stopped in this thing that shouldn't have been, but still is. And how could it possibly be when he was *just last night* sitting on the couch laughing, eating, watching a boring show on Netflix. When he was slogging toward bed—teeth brushed and flossed—so bland, so diligent, so expectant of another day. The room hums with that lost expectation, that *might-have-been*, that *should-have-been*, that last night on earth that now seems so unexpectedly insufficient.

I've been at this table dozens of times—different places, different people, different ages, different circumstances, different lists, different what ifs, different dead bodies in the other room. But it's a place we hover—navy blue shadows to someone else's tragedy. Occasionally in these instances, one of the family members speaks to me. Would I like some coffee? Do I see the tissue box? Do I have any idea of why this might have happened?

"No," I always say, the same answer to all the questions, as though they bear equal weight.

When the coroner arrives, our job is done. He will handle the body, the family, any further paperwork.

We walk from the house of sorrows back to the ambulance. Sometimes the shadow is easy to shrug off. We get another call or fill up the gas tank or grab a bite to eat. But sometimes their hurt seeps into my own skin. I enter my own house, my own bed, talk to my own wife. And I hear a little girl's crying. Not the tears of my child who is still soundly and innocently asleep. Though I know that with a different twist of fate, it could have been her, us.

And a piece of their mourning enters, coming to rest at my own table.

PART II

Hard Laughter, Round One

The Tortoise and the Hare: A Rethinking

In Aesop's fables, the hare always gets a bad rap—that cocky rabbit lounging around while the tortoise wins the day. There's no doubt that slow and steady is great for corporate ladder climbing or New Year's resolutions or even high school. But in a job where you need to be able to jump up from a recliner where you're watching *The Great British Bake Off* and rush to a nearly dead man who needs drugs and intubation and resuscitation—all in as few minutes as possible—the hare gets a shot at redemption.

Truth: We spend a certain amount of time being bored.

Also truth: We spend a much smaller, but more important, amount of time trying to stop catastrophe. And we're not talking early-onset catastrophe either. Most of the time the momentum has already built; we enter the scene mid-tsunami.

You could be sitting around watching cat videos on your phone at the station. Or maybe you're posting, which means that you've been sent somewhere central to wait until a call comes in. If you're lucky, you're posting at the

Dairy Queen parking lot, just trying to enjoy your Reese's Blizzard in peace. And then, bam, four minutes later you're standing in a puddle of blood, trying to put some-body's insides back, well, inside.

It takes a certain type. (Usually a type who can finish the Blizzard afterwards.) Don't worry, if you're a tortoise, you're probably making more money than I am. But it turns out there's a place for us hares after all.

That place is generally in an ambulance on our way to what we think is a dumb call—something like an old guy who can't pee. No lights, no sirens. Because, while not being able to pee is surely uncomfortable, it's not some-thing that makes us stop traffic.

Before that call—the one with the man who can't pee —I'd been hanging out on my phone, watching comedians. I'm still thinking about the jokes, smiling; we're still moseying along, stopping for lights like everyone else, when dispatch comes on to say that CPR has been initiated. CPR? For the guy who can't pee. Lights go on, sirens, speed goes up, adrenaline too.

Within minutes we're on a chaotic scene with an unconscious, unbreathing, nearly-gone man. A volunteer firefighter is outside waiting for us, while another man (who I think is another firefighter, though he's actually the patient's father) performs CPR.

The patient has collapsed near the table and our first order of business is to move him to a place where one of us can keep doing CPR while the other gets a line with epinephrine going. (Epi is good at jumpstarting hearts.) But the guy is huge. I take one arm. The father (who I still think is a volunteer firefighter) takes the other and we begin dragging him away from the kitchen table where he collapsed. Another couple of volunteer firefighters arrive and together we move him to the center of the floor. My partner takes over CPR and I tell a young, brand new volunteer firefighter to get some oxygen going. But he doesn't know how, and hooks it up wrong.

That takes me a few seconds to fix—precious seconds in a scene that is moving fast and getting faster. As I'm fixing things and starting the IV in order to give medication, my partner inserts an i-gel. This is a simple tube that anyone can put into a throat to provide oxygen, but it's not working right. We take it out, and I try to intubate the patient (which involves putting a more reliable, but much harder-to-insert tube down his trachea). That doesn't work either. I can't reach the epiglottis and, for whatever reasons —his weight, lack of breathing, lack of heart rate, I don't know—I can't get the throat open enough to get the tube inserted properly. I could keep going at it, and sometimes medics get caught in that loop ("I've got to get the tube; I've got to get the tube"). But a tube won't do much good to a dead guy, so it's back to the i-gel. It works this time, though none of us could tell you why. His color goes from blue to pink. I give another dose of epi. The heart is moving slightly, but still not enough to count as living. With four other guys, I roll the patient onto a backboard and then we move him to the cot and out to the ambulance.

Normally, on a call like this, my partner (an EMT) will drive, but right now I need him in the back of the ambulance with me because while I give more epi, my partner needs to suction out the patient's airway (when people are dying they fill up with fluids—all the things from their stomachs and everywhere else come up into their throats). A volunteer firefighter goes up front to drive. He hasn't driven code three (lights and sirens) before and gasses it so hard that we all fall down. I tell him to stop and insist another volunteer go up and drive. I don't worry about people's feelings; I don't give training or encouragement.

It's not the time for that. These are moments of *doing*, and doing quickly.

My partner suctions. I give two more doses of epi. The patient starts gasping—trying to breathe. Will it be enough? Will we save the day? I don't know. We rarely find out. At the hospital, a team waits—doctor and nurses. Together we move the patient off the cot, onto a bed. And then our part in the catastrophe ends.

I sign off, fill out my paperwork, clean the ambulance.

And then it's back to YouTube, to Netflix, to British comedians or raccoon videos or Facebook or a real book. Back to quiet, to boredom.

If I'm lucky, I can even squeeze in a nap like the hare that I am.

Until, of course, the tones go off again.

A Paramedic's Sonnet to
Nitrile Gloves

With a Shout-out to Elizabeth Barrett Browning

How do I love thee? Let me count the ways.

I love thee to the depth and breadth and height

My hands can reach, which include body folds (inches deep) and flaps of severed skin.

I love thee to the level of every day's most

Quiet need, from spit and blood to sweat and throw up.

I love thee freely since men strive against right in bar brawls and street fights.

I love thee purely

as thou canst be removed and my hands untouched by nature's most vile creations.

I love thee with the passion—no, duty—put to use.

In my old griefs, and with a new medic's faith.

I love thee with a love I didn't lose when the thrill of sirens and speed went dull.

I love thee with the breath, smiles, tears, of all my career;

and, if I make it home without disease or infection caught between my fingernails,

I shall but love thee better after my shift.

Party Stories

"You must have some *stories*."

It's what people say to me at parties and get-togethers. And it's true. I do have stories—many of them painfully boring: *Once upon a time an old woman fell down and we picked her up. The end. Once upon a time there was a fender bender where no one got hurt and the teen driver cried. The end.*

These make up the bulk of my calls. Only a small percentage involve anything even close to life or death emergencies, and many of those have disappointingly depressing endings. So, at parties I usually default to the funny or the strange.

I tell them about the time a dancer fainted at a strip club. We were posting nearest to the club, so we got sent. However, after the call went out several units radioed in saying, "Hey, we're really close. We could take it if you need us to." How nice. Interestingly, we don't get that response for the poopers or the fallers. No one ever seems to be close when someone has crapped all over the kitchen and slipped in it.

I tell them about the woman whose fat began to jiggle

on the cot in the ambulance, causing her so much discomfort that she asked me to hold it down during the drive. Which I did. They don't call us public servants for nothing.

I tell them about another woman who was experiencing abdominal pain. I began to palpate her stomach, only to realize that her breast was so large and so long that I was not, in fact, palpating her stomach at all. I have moved a shocking number of extremely large breasts in my day. I'm sure that would be impressive on any resume.

I tell them all the poop stories, like the fainting patient we found covered in poop. Just before the call, my partner had made the mistake of eating at Taco John's. So, while I struggled to hold up poopy guy, attempting to check his blood pressure, my partner went outside and barfed on the lawn.

I tell them about the time my partner stepped on poop —*human* poop, *inside* the house. And how he cleaned his boot off in their sink.

Poop always gets a laugh. As does other bad behavior.

I tell them about the night I went through the drive-thru at McDonald's. A little donation box hung outside the window in support of the Ronald McDonald house. But in an attempt to donate, drive, and accept a Happy Meal all at once, several potential donors had missed the box and a large amount of change shone from the pavement beneath the donation box. As we waited for our order, my partner got out of the ambulance and picked up the money. Not to return it to the Ronald McDonald house box. Nope. He pocketed it.

I tell folks about that high guy in California. When we picked him up, we helped the cops put him in restraints. Unfortunately, we didn't get them tight enough. As we drove, he started going nuts and soon enough, he had worked his way out of his restraints. I was driving and looked over to see my partner backing toward me through the walk-through into the front of the ambulance.

"Looks like you kind of lost control back there," I said.

"Yup," he agreed.

The patient started throwing stuff, then got on the radio and said something. I don't remember what, but something along the lines of, "Help! These ambulance guys are kidnapping me!" Well, not exactly. But we wouldn't be transporting him anymore, because as soon as I could, I pulled over. When we opened up the back, he came barreling out, sprinting free into the world. Where he now resides as king over a hippie nudist colony in San Francisco. Nope. Just kidding (probably). Actually, the police had to come and apprehend him again. Good times.

But the truth is that they're not all good times, not all great party stories full of poop, theft of children's charity moneys, and escaped addicts. The truth is that I have other stories I don't like to tell. They don't make people laugh. You can't choose a different adventure if you turn to another page.

In spite of this, maybe because of this, we take the good times when they come. And, no matter how many bodily fluids they involve, we let the good times roll.

Wrestles, Winning and Losing

Mud Pit
NAKED DIABETICS AND OTHER
WRESTLES I'VE HAD

We're not cops. We don't carry guns or Tasers or handcuffs. I didn't come into this job expecting hand-to-hand combat. I expected old people, crying children, blood and guts, and even death. But I never expected to hold another human being down against his or her will. Because I never understood how significantly a will could be altered.

Over the years, I've held down addicts and drunks, head wounds and psych patients, people fighting restraints in a helicopter that could go down if they win, people struggling to pull out the very tubes that are giving them breath. Equal parts intimate and irritating, hilarious and heart-breaking, desperate and dumb.

━━━

THE DISPATCH CODE COMES IN: "Diabetic problem."

On a good day that means that we walk in, give the patient orange juice, and they're fine within ten minutes.

On an okay day, they can't swallow, but we give a quick

IV with sugar water, which brings their sugar up in seconds; then they can eat.

On a bad day, we hold them down and start the IV. Not fun, but fast.

And on a really bad day, we walk into a dark room to find a woman on the bed—altered, combative, and stark stinking naked. I don't remember sheets.

None of which is necessarily her fault. When the body's sugars drop to a certain level, the brain suffers; it can't function normally. And it doesn't.

"Hey," I say. "What's going on?"

No response.

Okay, okay. Out comes the glucometer. "We just need to see your finger." A quick prick to test her. She pulls her arm back like a stubborn child resisting a shot. But she's not a child and she's not really resisting. She's in a different place. Her movements and actions could be those of someone dreaming, of someone haunted, of someone feral. Confused, disoriented, erratic, raw. It seems unfair to compare her behavior to an animal because in it is something so ragged and desperate, so deeply human. Just not the type of human ideal for sticking with needles. But stick her we must.

By this point, her sugar has dropped to a dangerous level. If it keeps dropping, she'll eventually lose consciousness. And once that happens (even before that happens) the threat of death is real and close. It's not our job in this moment to be judicious, compassionate, thoughtful, kind, patient, therapeutic, or even respectful (though I would argue that at the end of the day, saving someone who doesn't want to die is all of those things). Our one job is to get her sugar up to a level where she can think, eat, *live*.

Which makes our mission statement simple: Save patient.

The implementation is a little bit harder.

I get the prick, test her sugar, but now she's even less cooperative. Writhing, kicking, grunting. Our next job is usually to put a tourniquet around her arm, so we can clean her arm and insert a needle. Normally, we'll tape it there and run a dose of D50 (essentially sugar water). However, she is currently swinging her arms around, rolling on the bed, twisting, thrashing. I make a grab for her; she jerks away. My partner scrambles toward her on the doughy mattress; she lurches and hits.

Have you ever tried to wrestle a toddler who didn't want a shot? Imagine doing that with a 180-pound woman who's nude, reckless, and . . . slimy. It might not seem like the nicest word, but it feels like the most accurate one. When the blood sugar drops to a certain level, the body produces an excess amount of adrenaline. This causes the obvious problems of fighting and attempted flighting. It also causes a whole lot of sweat. We struggle to get a hold of her arm; this woman is slick.

She's in her bed, whipping her slippery body around. I crawl on and grab her arm, twist the tourniquet around it. But IVs can be difficult to stick even when a patient is calmly sitting on a table and *not* trying to punch you in the face. At this point there's no way I can get out a needle and have things end well. We have to get her under control. You know, so we can give her the medicine that will help her get under control. (And that, Alanis Morissette, is what we call ironic.)

My partner—a huge guy—grabs at her other limbs, swatting and slipping until, eventually, he drapes his full 260 pounds across her legs and torso. A biblical-level struggle for a moment of stillness. I swab the arm, insert the needle (yup, I got it). Normally, I would tape the IV and let the medicine do its thing, but she's flowing with sweat. No tape on earth is going to hold. Not to mention the fact that she's pulling and squirming, trying to fight free; and I still want to get through this experience without getting elbowed in the nose, kicked in the crotch, or stabbed with my own IV. So instead of tape, I pin her hand under my knee, leaning against her arm and shoulder, gripping her tightly while I hold the IV in with my free hand. She wriggles and pushes, whimpering and moaning. Until she doesn't. Regains herself. Sits up as my partner and I stagger away, sweaty and smelly now ourselves.

Naked and fluid-soaked on the bed, she is reborn. Plus forty years of embarrassment. Because newborns couldn't care less about being in their birthday suits on a bed with two medical who-knows-whos standing in the room.

We hand her a blanket.

Our job done, my own memory clouds. I don't remember what happens next. I can't remember if there are family members there to help, if she gets dressed, if she thanks us or apologizes.

I know we don't leave until she eats. The D50 doesn't last forever, and we don't want to be back in an hour.

Maybe a mother or son or husband brings her something. Maybe she rummages through the refrigerator herself. Eventually she'll hold an apple or cheese stick or sandwich to her mouth—alert, alive.

We walk out the door.

Night Life

Note from Jean: Originally this essay was titled "Another Day in Paradise," and it was about a day in the grind of EMS. However, after we'd worked on all these essays and this book was just about to go into publication, I read Kevin Hazzard's amazing book, A Thousand Naked Strangers: A Paramedic's Wild Ride to the Edge and Back. *I had intentionally put off reading this book until I was done with James's essays so that I wouldn't inadvertently "copy" Mr. Hazzard. Well, guess what? Hazzard also had a chapter titled "Another Day in Paradise," and it was also about the grind of a day in the life. I sat and stared at the page. I even took a picture of it. There were already a lot of common themes and experiences shared between the two books, although James and Kevin (can I call you Kevin? I feel like I can call you Kevin) have very different personalities. But, staring at that page, I couldn't believe that these two different men telling their two different stories about their lives as paramedics would happen onto the same sardonic title. It showed how much is shared in the lives of these men and women in EMS (which bleeds—no pun intended—into the Fire and Police departments as well). All this to say that, although we let Kevin Hazzard (and Phil Collins) keep their titles to themselves, this essay is about a day (or night, as it were) in the life of a difficult job—a day that isn't really paradise, a day when people don't always behave as they should— whether it's the EMS team or the people they're picking up. A day that is so typical in its essence that two people who've never met, or even found each other on Twitter (at least not at this writing), would sarcastically stumble onto the same title for an essay with a shared theme.*

IT RAINS.

The call comes in as shortness of breath. Sounds urgent, right? It's not. When we arrive, the patient is suffering, not from an asthma or heart attack, but from a simple stomach bug. She is mostly vomited out by the time we arrive, though she dry heaves continuously throughout the call. It's not that I don't feel sorry for her; it's just that this call is not any kind of emergency.

Most aren't.

But we take her to the hospital anyway. If people want to go, we take them. That's our job—taking people who want to go. It's not what I *thought* my job would be. I thought it would be strokes, head bleeds, sepsis, trauma, plane wrecks, train wrecks, weapon wounds. Instead, we spend most of our time with falls, hyperventilation, broken bones, broken hearts, broken minds. Important things sometimes, but things that don't need ambulance transport.

Like this woman's stomach bug.

My main beef with this patient is not actually that she called, but that when we get her into the ambulance and I hand her a vomit bag, she ignores it, and somehow finds more in her stomach to hurl all over the ambulance. Even my young children have mastered the concept of a barf bag. Yet many of my patients seem unschooled in the process of putting their mouths over the bag instead of puking wherever they stand, lie, or sit.

A better man might remind himself that she could have a good reason for calling, an underlying medical condition, a tendency toward dehydration, some cause that means we really do need to be there. A better man (or maybe even me on a different night) might find meaning in bringing comfort to the suffering, but I find that instead it just feels like now two of us are suffering instead of one. I guess it's the type of night I've decided to have.

When she is safely deposited at the hospital and we have cleaned up all the vomit (school janitors have nothing on us), another call comes in.

Leg pain. Yes, it is just as vague as it sounds. The patient tells me that this pain has been going on for days (essentially, the definition of a *non*-emergent call), but tonight, after doctor's offices and urgent care clinics have closed down, he finally decides it is the perfect moment to make a call. We arrive shortly after. He walks to the ambulance, refusing the cot we offer.

Importantly, he wants to be taken to a nearby hospital that is across the state line. Why?

Because he has a warrant out for his arrest.

The truth is that police actually beat us to the scene, but they didn't want to arrest him before we took the patient to the hospital. Why?

Because if they do, the city or state will have to pay for his medical bills. So they let him ride on his own dime (well, likely the federal government's). When he wants to go to a different state, they're unconcerned. "We'll get him the next time." And they will.

We head across the Mason-Dixon Line and, upon arrival at the ER, the man who insisted on walking to the ambulance suddenly insists he cannot walk at all. We roll him out on the cot, and it looks like he's working toward some kind of Emmy with this new level of performance—moaning, woeful looks, grabbing his knee. The thing is, if I wanted to see a show, I'd go to the movies. What he doesn't seem to understand is that it makes no practical difference to me whether he's suffering or not. If he claims he hurts, it's my job to take him to the hospital, to roll or walk him through those automatic ER doors, and then to say good-bye. He can make his Oscar bid on the cot or strut through like the free felon that he is. Either way, my job is complete. At least until he calls a few nights later. EMS taxi at your service.

Though if the hospital calls any time soon, we won't be available for transferring (not that a transfer for this guy would likely be approved—he'll have to find his own ride back over the state line). Our next call is a pediatric psych. Depressing, every one. And depressingly frequent.

Right before bedtime a fifteen-year-old girl tells Grandma she's going to get the gun. Grandma calls us, as she should. But Grandma is not the legal guardian. That person is at work, and Mom is in jail. None of which matters (except that it all absolutely matters, just not in that very moment). All that matters in that one moment is that when you threaten to hurt yourself, you get a nice ride to the hospital, whether you want one or not.

This girl, however, refuses to let us evaluate or even touch her. That's fine by me; she can ride with police (I guess it's their turn). And she does.

Which frees us up for a birthday house call. When you spend your days in a wheelchair and it's time to get trans-ferred to bed, well, your husband usually helps you. Tonight, though, he calls us for the job, explaining that he didn't want to take a chance on his wife falling—not on her birthday. If only we'd worn party hats and brought cake.

(Do I sound like a jerk? It happens sometimes, and by this point in the night, I'm feeling a little grumpy. Also, I'd like to point out that even when I'm a jerk in my heart, I'm not a jerk to my actual patients; I still play nice.)

Not that he doesn't have reason to fear falls—birthday or otherwise. As demonstrated by our next call.

It's still raining when we leave. Pouring buckets into huge puddles on the road.

We find our next patient planted squarely in a puddle on the sidewalk. Wearing nothing but a nightgown. She's next to her wheelchair, but can't get back in. Apparently, she'd taken her dog out to do his business. And somehow slipped out of her wheelchair. When we arrive, a disabled man is yelling at her, trying to tell her how to get up. It's pretty ineffective.

We lift her back into her wheelchair and I figure it's time to put my cape back on and head out into the night, but she looks at my female partner and tells us, "Oh, *she's* going to get me out of these clothes." No asking, just a demand. I'm glad it's not me.

Our next patient is also thoroughly soaked. And high as a kite. If kites were half-naked things that hollered at strangers and themselves. He's wearing only shorts, standing by a fence and shouting incoherently. When we put him on the cot, he soaks it through.

Just another day in paradise.

Another night packed end to end with calls that use and often abuse the system. If I had to guess, I would say that at least half our calls (maybe more) are connected to drug use or crimes. Others come from alcohol abuse, depression, suicide threats, domestic violence, barroom fights. We also get indigestion misinterpreted as chest pain, anxiety misinterpreted as chest pain, boredom misinterpreted as chest pain. The tired, the cold, the uncomfortable. Bring them to us and we'll give them a ride. Because sometimes you want to go where everybody knows your name (and now I've gone and mixed my song metaphors).

But we don't want to know your name, not if you don't need to be here. And a lot of nights we aren't in the mood to serve up comfort or companionship. Maybe we should be. Maybe we should rise above, give to those who are aching, even if it is in an invisible or non-emergent way. But when you're cleaning a cot some guy didn't need to pee on, it gets a little tough.

Even so, I try to find the importance in it—the lift assist, the transports to psych units, the guy who can walk until he enters the ER. And the thing is—some of it matters. I mean, it must, right? And sometimes I stumble on it—that nugget of shared humanity. Calling someone by name, chatting with people about their kids, holding a hand. Being there when someone really needs me. Sometimes I remember people's sadness, my own weakness, that there might be underlying reasons for the things people do. Sometimes I remember that my life is good, and that I can spread a little bit of that to someone else.

But sometimes I miss it.

Sometimes I just want people to vomit into the bag, to use their perfectly capable legs, to call their doctor during the day, to have appropriate equipment or skills for falls, to live in assisted care facilities if they always need assisted care, to go to bed at night, to stay off drugs, to stop cussing at strangers, to stay in when it rains, and—for the love of all that draws breath—to keep their clothes on. Is that too much to ask?

I drag home, exhausted from doing something that feels like nothing, and go to sleep.

In eleven hours, I will go back and do it all again.

In eleven years, I will wonder what has kept me going

and if it can continue. The thrill of the sirens is long gone, but something remains, some desire to help those who cannot help themselves. Those of us who gather enough fragments of light will keep on, and those who don't will move on—to become grocery clerks or real estate agents or preachers. Occasionally, I dabble in other interests, wonder if I could grow a business, program a computer, invest in the rental market.

Maybe one day it will become too much and I will train to do something else. Maybe one day I will lose all the fragments of light, maybe one day I will walk away. But not tonight. Tonight—again—I put on my boots, kiss my children goodnight, and walk out the door.

Broken Nose Circles

James and J.K. Pace

A story.

On repeat.

She runs out of the house with no shirt on, no bra either. She and her little boy. She begs to sit in the cop car because she is still afraid of her boyfriend—the man who ripped off her clothes. The man that beat her so badly that her actual clothing was torn from her body. He's not there anymore. It'd be easier to arrest him if he was, but he's fled the scene.

The police take pictures, assess the house, acquire enough evidence for them to use should evidence be needed. The apartment is wrecked—furniture knocked over and smashed, glass all over the floor along with splintered wood.

She is bruised and shaking, but not otherwise broken. Crying, she tells both paramedics and police that she thought she was going to die. I can tell that she actually believes it—actually thought she might die. Tonight. In her own house. With her son watching. And she could have. It's always a possibility in violent cases like this. We've seen dead girlfriends and wives. Her boy is with her—maybe five or six years old, all physical details lost to my memory except that age.

She wraps something around herself, maybe a blanket. And presses charges. The police proceed.

Before it goes to court, however, the charges are dropped. Nobody is surprised. Nobody bothers with outrage or sorrow. It's an unhappy ending we've all seen before. Though 'ending' is the wrong word.

ANOTHER CALL. A different couple. Like the scene of a cheap slasher movie. Blood splattered on the wall, dripping down in rivulets. From a boyfriend and girlfriend fighting well past the point of first blood, so that it sprays in showers across furniture and appliances, floors and lights.

AND ANOTHER. A stripper in a field with a man. She tells him 'no.' He beats her up. She runs, calls from the field (as she should). We find her there, among the barren rows. Shaken, but mostly safe. Luckily.

A BABY. Several actually. Brain bleeds. Different calls. Different times. Too many innocent faces to separate them now. Too many different stories that don't line up to remember them all. One mother sings a song to the baby before we leave. Love? Guilt? Overcompensation for a crime? Insanity? Actual innocence? I'll never know. It's not part of my job to know. I'll never know who shook the babies, hit the babies, dropped the babies. But there the babies are, in an ambulance with strangers. Parents receiving the news that they will no longer have custody over this child until a full investigation is complete.

⊂▭⊃

AND THIS IS the part where James's narration ends, and I (Jean, the writer) try to make something of it. This is the part where I am asked to form this into an essay—a creative work with a beginning, middle, and end. Perhaps a turn or twist, a bit of character development. An artistic piece that has been filtered and sifted, formed into something coherent—beautiful or ugly—but complete.

Only here I fail.

Charges withdrawn or never made. Love sworn off then reignited. Repeat customers to the ambulance agency. Around and around in that wobbling loop. Hello to the bruised, good day to the broken.

At every call in this state, the police ask three questions.

One. Do you want to file for an emergency protective order (more commonly known as a restraining order)? If you do, they will take you, immediately, to the police station and help you fill it out. If you decide later, or at any point, you can file for this protective order.

Two. Do you want to be taken to an abuse center? If you do, they will help get you there.

Three. Did you receive victim's rights information? This is a packet of resources given to the victim by the police officer. Among the resources is a list of rights the person has as a victim of domestic violence. Once the officer gives and explains the information, the victim initials and signs with a date and a witness signature. All this goes with the report.

But victims do not rush to the courts; they do not rush to get protective orders; they do not rush away from their homes or their abusers. It is partly what it means to be abused—to have your heart turned inside out, twisted around. More often than charges, the victims who called—upon seeing their abuser arrested—will cry out, "No, don't take him." In situations like this there is little to be done. The county attorney can issue a charge, along with a warrant for the abuser. But if the victim doesn't want the charges to go through, they might get dropped. If the victim doesn't show up in court or is unwilling to witness, then the case won't go anywhere either.

It's up to the victim. And often the victim simply isn't in a place to make big change happen.

And so, this essay ends as it has begun. Going in circles. Holding out open arms. Staring through the cracked holes of so many broken hearts, and hoping they'll one day be sealed.

PART IV

Seeking Humanity

Of Blood and Bone

J.K. Pace

A suicide. An acquaintance from our circle. Gunshot to the head.

People plan meals and cards, make sure the spouse has somewhere to go that is not the home.

It's late at night, but my husband makes a few calls of his own and meets another friend—a mortician—at the house.

For a cleaning job that few could do.

They enter the workout room, sticky with blood, the scent of body and rubber mingling. The mortician has poured an absorbent solution on the biggest pool of blood, much like a school janitor would do with vomit. As it slowly soaks into a more cleanable substance, they each take paper rags and disinfectant, moving through the room. Splatters of blood flow in lines on the floor, splashes on nearly every surface in the room.

They hunt and remove every drop, every reminder.

But gunshot wounds leave more than blood. Chips of bone picked from the walls, small pieces of hair stuck to the floor with globs of blood or bits of flesh.

Rag after rag, they move systematically, carefully. Neither man with a bachelor's degree, neither a high wage earner, both minivan drivers, middle-class dads. Piece after piece of remnant and loss, all in the form of tissue and fluid. They remove; they disinfect. They cannot clean memories, cannot erase loss, cannot turn back time, cannot solve depression, cannot undo, unmake, unbind. But they can wipe; they can scrub. They can create space. For steps forward.

No one has to step into that space. No one has to heal, to move ahead, to forgive, to remember, to forget. But they make the room for it anyway.

Few know they've done it. It doesn't go on Facebook or Instagram. They receive no award, no Christmas bonus, not even an hourly wage. Neither of them would talk to you about it, even if you asked. That is why I—the wife of one of them—am the one writing the essay; I am the one remembering this night. Few even think to wonder what happens to the bodies of the dead. Few consider what must have been done from the darkest hour of the now-dead to the darkest hour of the ones left living.

But some think about it.

And those who live come home.

When they do, they extend the deepest, quietest thanks.

An empty room. Maybe it will be opened again. Maybe it won't. A small choice for a fellow human to make. Because one night a paramedic and mortician showed up well past dark on a night off. To pick bits of blood and bone from the walls.

A Thousand Ways to Die

My wife found him on her way to the store—our elderly neighbor whom neither of us knew. Lying there by his leaf blower, pale, unmoving. She drove past, stopped, reversed. So odd that he was lying down on his lawn like that. And so very still. She put on the hazards, left the kids in the car. Called me.

People always do.

So many bodies in so many positions in so many places.

Most aren't glamorous.

Most aren't exciting.

Plan to die on your recliner. Maybe in your bed. The truth is that you'll be lucky if you do. Death isn't the place to get interesting. Don't go in for guns or motorcycles or some kind of grand fall off of something. Just keep it simple. Preferably clean. A circle of loved ones ushering you over to the other side. Yeah, do that.

As though you get to choose.

As though I do.

And so we'll die, as people do.

We'll die with our bodies betraying us. Pools of sweat or pools of blood. Fluids congealing in usually-busy intersections, bathrooms, bedrooms, beds. Naked in a pond of diarrhea. And someone, hardened from too many shifts on too many nights in a row, will call the coroner and return to his ambulance to finish his hamburger. I won't say that it was me.

We'll die, leaving nature to feed on us. Hunched over in the garage and covered with maggots. Found in a windy Wyoming field by a rancher on his rounds. Thrown into woods from cars or motorcycles.

We'll die wishing nature had taken us instead of being dragged through a parking lot, or collapsing onto a concrete sidewalk, or crushing head first into the metal of a steering wheel.

We'll die in unlucky, seemingly impossible ways. Like on a paper route when your own car rolls backward, pinning you beneath it. The weight, the pressure, taking your breaths until you suffocate; and that is how my partner and I find you.

We'll die on nights we fully planned to live. Perhaps bashed against a train that was left inexplicably parked on an unmarked country crossing. Its immovable hulk, black as the night—an invisible iron wall that absorbs the crush of your car, that takes with it the beats of your heart, the rush of your breath. That leaves a crew of emergency workers to peel you out. A chain hooked from the firetruck to your bumper, pulling it from the side of the train like a bent accordion. While I thread my way between the train cars to reach you, squeeze part of my body through your car window to check for a pulse—dead, so dead, smells of fluids burning from the car, glass everywhere. And you probably never even knew what hit you, or rather, what you hit.

We'll die from age and weight and sickness. Five hundred pounds filling your veins, pressing your heart. Sugars dropping and with them your consciousness.

We'll die from good things and bad things in all the wrong proportions—sugars and medicines, needs and wants. A dozen flavors of addiction. Sleeping pills, narcotics, methamphetamines. Breath too slow or heart too fast. All ashes in the end. Sometimes we can help with Narcan, the bag valve mask, chest compressions. But if the brain has died, then no heart thump or lung pump will ever bring you back. Not to yourself.

We'll die from stubbornness. One call from a loved one to the ambulance, but you refuse to go. Another call several hours later when you're coughing up blood. You tell me that it's Kool-Aid and insist that we leave without you. I look into your face and say, "This could kill you." A final call, early morning. Now it's the coroner who makes his way to your house.

We'll die in filth. A hoarder dead in his bed, surrounded by things piled almost as high as the covers. No path to walk, so that when I arrive I stumble over the mountains of clothes and trash, feces and papers, blankets and bugs in order to get an EKG strip to show a heart that no longer trembles.

We hope not to die in violence.

Our own. A shot to the head on a country road. Or an apartment balcony, alone during the Christmas season. Or in an alley after a standoff with the police.

Or the violence of others. A small business, an angry employee. As we drive up to the building, we see the first body, cradled in blood, outside of the door—gunshot to the head. Two more as we walk further in. All head shots. All with a heartbeat that fades as time passes because of the swift loss of blood. All without hope.

"Pick a patient," the first paramedic on scene tells me. And I do.

Some mornings, we die in love or simple carelessness, or a crappy combination of both. So that when a dog runs along ice you cannot see in the early dusk, you run after him, falling through into the frigid waters.

We die on the floor, in bed, on chairs, while watching TV. The horrible and the ordinary wrapping together, taking us to the same place in the end. We die with lights flashing. We die in perfect darkness. Sometimes in a blast to the heart, sometimes from a too-long pause of the lungs. Slow, fast. A thousand ways.

And sometimes we die with dignity, even sweetness. As though breath itself falls asleep. Those standing beside take in that last gasp, then let out their own lonely sigh. Peace settling over the room. A life well lived, worn long, happy. I stand back in those moments, barely needed, probably not wanted.

Which is exactly what I would choose. If ever I get to.

Wreck

J.K. Pace

Just shy of two years into our marriage, we come up on a wreck about three minutes from James's parents' house. James sees it first and says, "Crap."

"What?" I ask, and suddenly the scene opens up in front of me magically, as if it wasn't really there a few seconds ago. My rational mind knows it must have been or we would have heard the crash, but to the rest of me, the fact that it is there just a few feet past the red light, seems mystical—as if it all must have fallen from the sky—the gray smashed car, the ring of people around it, the shards of glass reflecting off the road in the sun.

Even when I think about it later, I will not be able to recall hard details—a man stood there, the door of the car hanging just so, a woman with a red striped shirt in the middle of the crowd. Instead, it will always feel blurry to me, like a child's drawing—peach-colored heads bobbing against blue August sky, pale legs walking on black earth, and there in the middle of it all, a gray car, crushed, but in my memory I will never be able to see the dents in the side, the deformity of the frame, deep scrapes in the paint—only thousands of pieces of glass in the light.

I look at the wreck and think, *Oh well, cars crunch so people don't.* This sings through my mind in a careless way. At the beginning of our trip from Colorado to Utah, James and I had somehow started talking about cars. "They make cars to crunch," he had told me. "So people don't. A lot of cars have crumple zones in the front and back, or the engine is made to drop out—and it looks like there's a lot of damage, but the vehicle absorbs the impact and keeps people safer." I had taken his word for it. James has seen his share of crunched cars and the people in them.

Now, in the backseat, our ten-month-old, Hyrum, sits open-eyed and quiet as we wait at the light. I consider turning to James to laugh about how we were *just talking about how cars crunch so people don't,* but he's not paying attention to me. He's telling the stoplight "Hurry up and change," and scooting forward in jerky little inches, anticipating the green. When we finally get it, he shoots through the intersection and pulls over. It is only then that I realize there are no police cars or ambulances on scene yet. The accident has just happened. I am still not very concerned.

We park on the shoulder where several cars are already parked. It takes me several seconds to realize these are witnesses. There has been a wreck and there are witnesses.

James hops out of the car and my first instinct is to get Hyrum out of his car seat and go closer to James. But when I look toward the gray car, I see a small child—a baby really, a few months older than Hyrum—lying on the pavement. The baby's small brown limbs rest loose and still on the ground. Something inside me stops. I had been excited to get to see this wreck, excited to watch James at work, excited to have such a fun little story to tell our family and friends. I hadn't realized all of this, but when I look at the baby on the road, I become aware of all those feelings as they leave in a gush. I open Hyrum's door, but don't take him out. He watches me—peaceful even after a six-hour drive. It gives me an eerie, sad feeling and I pray suddenly and fervently that the little boy on the pavement will live—because if someone else's son is allowed to die, then what is there really to protect my own?

In front of me, a redheaded woman is on a cell phone —pushing the buttons, shaking the phone when no one answers, then stomping her feet in a frenzied way. Later when I recall the wreck, I will not remember the sound of the sirens approaching or the whir of the helicopter landing, but I will remember the stampede of this woman's feet.

I assume at first that she is a witness—a panicky witness it seems—with four small children a few paces from me lined up against the guardrail, the oldest around seven years old. She calls again, gets no answer, and pounds her feet fast on the ground, letting out a strangled sort of squeal. And it occurs to me all at once that someone has hit the gray car and that right next to the woman is a Tahoe with the front crushed, tilting slightly because one of the tires has completely deflated.

Her second oldest child is hanging close to her and saying, "Mommy, our car is all crunchied up."

The redhead touches his hair and breathes deeply, "I know, honey. It's okay; you had your seatbelts on." And in another moment, the motherly calmness is gone, and she is back at the phone, punching at the numbers with an intensity that seems to want to believe reaching her husband can make all this, or at least the very bad parts of it, go away.

I have lost James in the crowd. I look toward the gray car and see him—back to me—bending into the passenger seat.

I offer the woman's children something to eat. The oldest chooses a peanut butter chocolate granola bar and eats only a little before starting to whimper and giving it to her brother. She is the only one of the four who seems to understand why her mother is so upset.

A plain-clothes officer has arrived with a small first-aid kit and is calling to a partner to get something to open an airway. The baby on the road is now partially undressed and I think, "Oh no, he's not breathing right; they'll have to put a tube down his throat." It seems strange to me now that it never occurred to me that it might be for someone else—that there might be others in the car in much worse shape than the baby they were able to quickly extricate and work.

A man who has been helping comes over and I ask him how the baby is. "Oh—he's okay, but that girl doesn't look so good." The girl is the woman in the passenger's seat. But oddly—sadly—older patients don't strike me as terribly important; I rejoice that the baby is okay and let the other, bad news find a peaceful place in the back of my thoughts.

When the police and ambulances arrive, James takes off his gloves and comes over to me. I say something to him, and he replies, his voice straight and honest, "A kid in the backseat is dead. And the woman's on her way." This new knowledge bangs in my brain and stops on the word *dead*—a word which snaps with closure, so unlike *life*, which trails off in a filmy way without any kind of solid definition. I feel simplistically that a child cannot be dead—surely not from *this*. This was just an *accident*. The EMS team will take the boy out of the car and move his head and his airway will open, or maybe they will have to do CPR, but surely this will revive him. This is what rescuers do on TV. On TV someone can be dead for several minutes and *voila*—in a flurry of medical personnel and modern technology, he is revived. This is how it works.

I stare at James and ask, stupidly, "There's a kid in the backseat?"

"Yeah."

"Are you sure he's dead?"

"He's not breathing, and I can't find a radial pulse." And the boy's head is down, and the metal of the car is so twisted that James cannot reach his neck to get a carotid pulse. "Side impacts are bad." This is James's conclusion. This is all he can offer me.

"And the one on the ground?" I ask.

"He's crying. That's good—some broken bones probably, but he'll be okay." Still he says this as if the other one would not be okay, and still I cannot believe it.

The first book I cried over was *Bridge to Terabithia*. The little girl in the book drowned and in my eight-year-old imagination, I kept thinking the boy in the book must be having a bad dream or something, and at the end the girl would wake up and the girl would be alive, and everything would be fine. When the book ended with the girl still dead, I cried and cried so hard in my room that later that night I was embarrassed to go downstairs and have anyone ask why I'd been crying. Because what would I say? *A girl died in a book.*

I feel that now—that denial, that embarrassment that I care, that *Why does this bother me*—*I don't know this boy. I have not even seen him.*

The baby is naked on the ground now—and also a boy. I look at Hyrum, still secure in his car seat and spookily content there. I administer sunblock to the redhead's pale-skinned children while the woman calls her husband over and over again. "I know I didn't run a red," she blurts to one of the witnesses who is standing close by and holding one of the children.

I want to put a kind arm around the redhead's shoulders and say, *Of course you didn't. Of course you will not have to live with this for the rest of your life.*

Of all the people on this scene, I can most easily slip myself into her skin—a young mother, busy and distracted. I have always had a small fear of driving, a fear that in some ways, has become more agitated in these first nervous months of parenthood. I have always thought too long after the fact about small slips of concentration, the car in my blind spot I almost veered into, the man on the motorcycle we didn't see until we cut him off, the startling sound of the rumble strips when I'm tired but not yet asleep at the wheel, the spinning feeling in my stomach when the car hydroplanes over a puddle of water and I overcorrect, skidding slightly—the kind of lapses that happen to all of us all the time.

I watch the woman, still holding her phone, and feel very, very sorry for her. Whether it was her fault or not, she will eventually know a child is dead in that car. When the news announces a fatality, that sterile, terrible word will ring in her head for the rest of her life, and she will be too scared to drive, and worry about lawsuits, and—worst of all—wonder if she deserves to mother four healthy, beautiful children when someone else's has died.

James has returned to the gray car and is working with the other paramedics. Hyrum has finally started to fuss. I pull him out, as a bloodied man—the driver—is led to the ambulance right in front of me.

In a few more minutes, the baby, head and body secured in a mummy-like brace, will be stretchered to another ambulance. They have not yet extracted the dying woman from the car, but eventually she will be flown in the helicopter that waits some thirty yards from me. And after all this, we will get in our car and drive away. James will say, "I've never driven away from a scene in my own car." But that's just what we'll do. Goodbye police and EMTs and witnesses and redheads. Goodbye dead boy still pinched in the backseat of a car. Goodbye blood and glass, hot on the afternoon street. And when we get to James's parents' house, people will greet us with hugs and even after I tell them, *There was a terrible accident and a little kid died*, they will not understand and say, *How sad*, and then squeal about how much Hyrum has grown.

———

JAMES TELLS me later that evening that this is sometimes how it is—people die and no one really gets what that means. He tells me this wreck was hard for him too because even in his four years of EMS work, he has not found a small child already dead. He tells me, also, that he was the one who first knew it. After he realized the boy was gone, a group of people started trying to get the boy's door off so they could take him out. They turned to James and asked, "Shouldn't we help *him*?" And James, who had moved on—as all good paramedics must do—to the most serious living patient, had had to turn to them and say, "He's dead."

When James tells me this that night, the word *dead* flips again against my head. Again, I go through the moments in my life when my concentration waned for just a few seconds. I see the bicyclist who lost his balance and stumbled from the bike path almost in front of my car. I see the day I was lost in my thoughts when another driver started to merge into my spot, how I swerved into the side of the street where oncoming traffic could have been and slammed on my brakes too fast, fishtailing. I feel the sudden gusts of Wyoming's wind from that morning when I drove seventy-five miles per hour on I-80—the way the wind tossed the car over a foot or so, the way the panic rose in me so much that my breaths shortened and my body started to tingle.

I also wade through the time a few months earlier when James was looking for a different line of work because this one was so stressful, how we had no money, and how I kept thinking, "Why do bad things always happen to me, *to me, to me*? Remembering this fills me with guilt. I have my baby boy. I have full use of my limbs and head and body. I have my husband.

James tells me how the driver of the car—hurt himself —kept hovering over his unconscious wife, bending down and wanting to help her, unable to speak enough English to ask James questions or understand a lot of the talk buzzing around him. James tells me this in a voice that says he thinks he would feel the same way. He tells me he really wants the woman to live, because she was his patient, because she was someone's wife.

It gives me an unexpected glimpse into a part of James I didn't understand before—his anxiety about his job, his bravery, stamina, heroism, and—perhaps most of all—a glimpse into the sometimes futility of his work. Not everyone can be saved. He will not always be the hero. I feel proud of him because he does this anyway, and without cockiness or hardheartedness or any of the fronts that could protect him from some of the realness of it all.

━━

I HAVE BEEN on calls with James once before. The first Christmas we were married, he had to work and I got permission to ride the ambulance with him. It was a slow day—a couple of elderly people who fell and broke their hips and a very old man who vomited and defecated on himself. The paramedics joked with the patients and chatted if they could. They secured them gently and compassionately onto a backboard and then into the ambulance. There was something warm and fuzzy about it. Although I knew James's job was not always so simple, in a way I think this is how I came to think about EMS—a smile and a stretcher and everything would be okay.

THAT NIGHT we need to go pick up a pizza, but Hyrum is tired of the car. My mother-in-law offers to watch him while we go. He's on the floor playing in front of a tall heavy cabinet and—as I leave with James, who I also don't want to be separated from—I catch myself thinking, "What if it falls on him while we're gone; what if this is the last I see him?"

That night I can't sleep, even with James's body wrapped tightly around mine. I think about the redheaded woman who is surely not sleeping tonight. I think of the dead child and keep stumbling through the dark unfamiliar room in order to hear Hyrum breathe. I think about James telling me how strange it felt to have the woman's unconscious but open eyes staring up at him while he held her airway open, while her bloody husband bent over her body, while they all waited for the ambulances to arrive. I think of the cleansered word "fatality" on the news that night. I imagine how, when they announced that the highway would be closed, people in their cars and living rooms would have groaned about delays—and I want to tell them, *No, a child died, pincered between the door and his seat.*

FIVE DAYS AFTER THE WRECK, when we're back home in Colorado, James is at work and I'm driving my sister-in-law and our friend, John, around town. I'm talking too much and taking a small, unfamiliar road. At an intersection that I think is a four-way stop, I stop and start to go again. The woman in the car to my right stops suddenly in the intersection gesturing angrily, and I realize I am not at a four-way stop, but have cut off the woman as well as the car to the south. I wave an apology and move as quickly as possible out of the way.

The woman would have hit the right side of my car. At twenty-five miles per hour—with seatbelts and Hyrum in his car seat—it is unlikely that anyone would have been killed. But the woman's car would have crunched neatly into my husband's sister and the man responsible for getting me and James together.

The rest of the drive home and for several hours afterwards, I see the woman's angry gestures and feel not scared exactly, not shaken in the usual way, but ashamed. Ashamed in a way that is part afraid, part relieved, many parts grateful, and one part something else—something awful and heavy, and avoided. This time.

A WEEK LATER, my mother calls to tell me that the newspaper reported that the woman in the wreck had died and that it looks like the driver of the Tahoe was at fault. I tell her this depresses me and that I wish she hadn't said anything. "Sorry," she says. "I thought you'd want to know."

"Yeah, it's okay. James just really wanted her to live,

and I just really didn't want the other woman to have to live with that."

"Well, maybe the article was about a different wreck."

I know she knows it wasn't.

Later when James comes home, I keep thinking about telling him, but don't—because his sister's still in town, because Hyrum is awake and ready to play, because these are the happy times, the ones that have the power to make death hard. But I know that eventually he'll read this and know, that eventually we'll have to look at each other awkwardly and he'll say, "She died, huh?" and I'll nod. And that much later, when he's thinking again about switching jobs, he'll tell me, "You know, the worst thing about being a paramedic is always having to wonder if there's something I could have done to make someone live." And when this happens, I'll reach across the table, touch his fingers, and wrap my own around them.

Making Space

A simple helicopter transfer hospital to hospital. Made less simple due to the fact that our patient is a five-year-old girl. Who wants her mother.

I don't blame her. If I'd been thrown from an ATV trailer and gotten a three-inch, skull-deep laceration to my head, I'd want my mother too. We are flying her because doctors at the hospital are worried about the possibility of a head bleed. They want her to get an assessment from a pediatric doctor who is familiar with head trauma.

Her only consolation prize is a trip in the small, loud helicopter, which neither charms nor fascinates her as it does some children. Realizing she's going to be in this contraption alone with a bunch of uniformed strangers who are wearing black latex gloves doesn't help.

She cries as we wheel her to it. She holds out her little arms as though reaching across the distance to get a final fleeting embrace from her parents (insert heartbreaking Hallmark imagery here). Her parents stand watching, also torn up about the fact that they won't be travelling with her.

We are upset too. In fact, we had tried to get a fixed wing airplane, which is large enough to transport patient, parent, and crew. But it couldn't get to us in time, leaving us with only the standard single-engine, two-blade Bell 206 helicopter (aka—a little one).

The truth is that sometimes we prefer to travel parent-free. Parents, as a matter of fact, can cause all kinds of problems. They panic when panic is not due, get angry at the people who are trying to save or revive their child, scream hysterically when we insert an IV, beg melodramatically that we please not hurt their baby (well, I was going to try to cause agonizing pain to this small human, but since you ask . . .). Throughout my career, I've asked more than one family member to leave the room when trying to insert an IV or intubation tube. Because a parent yelling "You're *hurting* her" in my ear is not helpful.

However, sometimes parents are golden. They calm and comfort our little patients, keep them still, make jokes, give smiles and hugs and all the good things. For this flight, it would have been nice to have smiles and hugs and all the good things.

We lift the patient's aluminum litter off the stretcher, slide it onto a special slot beside the pilot in the helicopter, then lock it in, securing her. She stops crying and settles into a miserable, tear-streaked stare. We give her a small headset that we can use to talk to her during the flight. She can also use it to talk to us if she chooses. She doesn't. She stares straight ahead, white bandage wrapped all the way around her head, large and almost cartoonish—the type of thing children might use when playing. It reminds me of my own daughters, and I hurt for her.

The helicopter leaves the ground in a roar, holding us tight—smaller inside than your average SUV, without even a touch of the spaciousness of a regular ambulance. Once inside we have no room for movement. The pilot sits up front, the patient to his left, a console in between. She rests on the litter, facing forward. The nurse and I sit in the very back, the end of the litter resting almost across my lap—as though we were in the back of a car with someone's seat reclined into us. We do not stand; we do not bustle; we have no room to do more than reach. We do this a lot, adjusting monitors, recording her vitals and scores every few minutes, and stretching over and around the patient from a somewhat unseen "right behind you" position. Although she is stable and still, she can't easily see any of us.

There seems very little that we can do, but I want her to know that we are here. I hold my hand out near the side of her seat. Her arm is dangling a bit off the litter and when she sees my hand, she reaches up and takes several of my fingers.

For a few moments, everything changes. The Rass scores, blood pressure readings, respirations, and coma scales fall away. We sit there together, the medical seeping away in the warm hand of a small girl, making space for the human.

PART V

Hard Laughter, Round Two

Dear Hollywood

Dear Hollywood,

WE *ARE* ALL FANTASTICALLY GOOD-LOOKING, so you got that part right.

I mean, except for those times when we haven't showered or slept for twenty-four hours.

Or maybe those few whose parents didn't spring for braces and teeth-whitening procedures when we were teenagers. But sure, we're all entirely buff, completely tan, swooningly tall, or patently adorable, depending on which is your absolute sexiest thing.

Yeah, that's us.

Though there may be a few other small details that you, dear Hollywood, have fudged just a bit.

First of all, we don't stab people in the heart with needles. Not even epi pens.

No matter how cool it might look. Even IVs go in at a boring slant, not a ninety-degree angle. We're not *skewering* people.

We avoid doing chest compressions on people's necks or abdomens. And our elbows don't bend.

CPR might save lives (sometimes, occasionally, because it buys a patient some time), but it doesn't work miracles every single time, or, well, most of the time.

And while we're talking miracles, could we please, please, please limit them to Christmas and Hallmark movies and stop involving asystole? Asystole is the heart rhythm more commonly known as flatlining. Guess what? It can't be shocked; or at least it can't be saved through a shock. Let me say this again for everyone everywhere (can I get an amen, my EMS brothers and sisters): When that little machine goes to a flat line on a movie, shocking them will NOT do anything to that heart. Unless a person's heart is in V-fib (quivering erratically) or ventricular tachycardia (organized mountains of electrical movement)—neither of which resemble a flat line in any way—a shock will NEVER start their heart again. Ever. Your time would be better spent dropping to your knees and praying than hollering for someone to pull out the Lifepak 15. Because a higher power is going to have more luck restarting a heart that has flatlined than an electric shock ever will. Amen and Amen.

And since we're praying, it might be well to discuss explosions. You know, those G-force level explosions with the billowing clouds of flame that people come running out of in movies. Yeah, they don't. And if they did, it would be with burns so severe that maybe they'd wish they hadn't. And you know how people are often getting literally thrown forward by those explosions? Do you know the amount of force necessary for this? To put it simply, it is easily as much force as a big old car crash. Meaning the impact of the explosion would be the same as the impact of a Mack truck hitting a pedestrian at a high speed.

Which means that, generally, the pedestrian doesn't get up and run away. Because usually their organs would just be all smooshed together into a piece of gloppy modern art.

And while we're discussing explosives and organ art, maybe we could also have a little conversation about jumping and/or falling from buildings. Generally speaking, this is a thing that we—as medical professionals—advise against. It tends to be extremely bad for your health, due to the fact that a simple jump, even from a height of, say, five stories would result in dozens of fractured and shattered bones at best, and your colon getting shoved to your throat at worst. Because, you see, when you hit the ground at that velocity, that is just what happens. All of your organs bang against each other as your bones bang against the pavement. The pressure makes you—how can I say this —mush. So, while in certain freak incidents one may survive a horrible fall, one does not generally stand up and run away afterwards. No matter who is chasing them. Even if it is a very bad guy. You can't run on bones crushed to dust, no matter your motivation. You can't breathe from lungs crammed with all your internal organs, even if your muscles are beautiful and glistening. Personally, I would recommend just letting the bad guy shoot you next time.

Which brings us to gunshot wounds. Movie makers (and movie viewers) *love* gunshot wounds. But, dear Hollywood, we all know you've never seen one. Or maybe if you have seen one, you haven't seen many. Or maybe if you have seen many (you haven't, come on), you haven't seen many at once. We have. Most of us don't want to ever again. The truth is they're not very glamorous. People don't often run or walk away after receiving one. Turns out people scream and cry a lot when shot by guns. And not for just a second. Also, you've got to remember that a bullet that enters and exits will leave a nasty exit wound. A bullet that doesn't have the force to exit can ricochet around in your body—bumping into organs and bones. And taking out a bullet doesn't make everything suddenly better.

But I get it. Gunshot wounds *sound* thrilling. I was excited to go on a call for my first gunshot wound, too.

Twenty-five years old and the call came in. The adrenaline, the thrill, the sirens and lights. Everything I'd been hoping for in my new career. They led us to a suicidal man who, drunk, had shot himself in the head. He'd aimed up at his chin, but when the gun went off, it had changed the trajectory of the bullet, tipping his chin up slightly, so that it missed his brain, but shot off half his face.

He sat in front of us—conscious, moaning, bone shards sticking out of flaps of skin. Every time he breathed, blood splattered as though he was sneezing it. (Fun fact: In the hustle to get him to the hospital, several of the ambulance cabinets had been left open. This meant that every single item inside had to be cleaned of blood splatters or—in the case of disposable equipment—thrown away.) Perhaps if every movie director had to stand in front of a faceless man wheezing gusts of blood onto every conceivable surface, action movies would play out differently. Or maybe...cut and fade to hospital.

Look, I'm not trying to ruin movies for you (well, maybe just a little), but dear Hollywood, it's more than just the way trauma looks. It's how it feels—too human, too animal, too raw, too wild. And the smells. So much more than blood. Hormones, heat, body odor, fear, car exhaust, fuel, alcohol, cigarettes, empty houses, rotting food, dog fur, cat poop, loneliness, desperation, vomit. All wrapped into a package no one ever wants to see again.

Which is why *you* wrap them into a package of Hugh

Jackman or Sean Connery, Angelina Jolie or Jennifer Lawrence. It's better that way. Prettier.

Because we all know that wounds are sexy. Ambulances are sexy too. At least in movies and TV shows. On screen, paramedics and EMTs are constantly hooking up in the backs of ambulances. Why not? Hot people in uniforms, a six- by three-foot cot in the back. Who wouldn't want to have sex there?

Answer: Anyone who's actually worked in one.

Because guess where you would never ever want to have sex?

The place where you've seen people hemorrhage, seize, vomit, bleed, cry, die. The place where they've had diarrhea, or babies, or both at the same time. The place where limbs have dangled, lives have dangled, blood has flowed, wounds have congealed. The place you clean (with a strong decontamination spray that you aren't supposed to let touch your skin) after every messy call. The place where blood splatters, pee splatters, snot splatters, spit splatters, poop splatters.

Do you want to have sex on a used adult diaper? Then you might want to have sex in an ambulance.

Do you want to have sex on the underside of a men's gas station toilet? Then the ambulance is the place for you to consummate a simmering slow burn relationship.

The rest of us will probably just go home to our spouses.

And, dear Hollywood, even if having sex where every bodily fluid from every dirty stranger you've ever transported is your kinky thing, guess what?

You'll get fired.

Listen, I'm really glad we had this talk, Hollywood. It means a lot to me that you'd listen. I mean, I know you're all glamorous and rich and stuff so it's great to know that

JAMES PACE & J. K. PACE

when I explain the actual facts to you, you'll pay attention to that one guy who gets paid maybe fifty grand a year to transport half the drug addicts on earth and maybe some other people who need it. So, thanks for hearing me, Hollywood. It means so much . . . (Wait; have you been on your cell phone this whole time? Are you legitimately tweeting gun wound GIFs to your followers? And is that a sexy paramedic costume in your Amazon cart? It only has, maybe, fourteen inches of fabric from top to bottom; do you have any idea how many germs that would expose you to? Could I just say . . . Nope. Okay. He's gone.)

Sincerely,

Someone who just got called to a motorcycle accident and will get paid about $20 total to pick up limbs off the freeway and drive them and their dying owner to the hospital

You Can't Put a Price On It
(But We Do Anyway)

They say you can't put a price on these things—the assists, the saves, even the losses. But they can and they do. Entire departments are, in fact, devoted to putting a price on the actions I perform. The interesting thing is that their price and my paychecks are vastly different things.

It's not something I can complain about (well, I can, and I do). But I knew what I signed up for when I signed on. Maybe at age twenty-four, I didn't realize everything—maybe I didn't realize that I was signing up for a career with very little upward mobility; maybe I didn't realize the frustrations and exhaustion I would encounter; maybe I didn't realize that a job where you are a "public servant" is a little more literal than you'd like it to be. But I did know, even then, that I wouldn't make a lot of cold, hard cash.

What I didn't realize was the number and disparity of calls I'd get. Things as inane as handing a bedridden patient her potato chips. Things as tragic as a mass shooting in which seven people were killed by a disgruntled worker. Each call (and every one in between) stressful and disillusioning in their very different ways, all of it heart-breaking.

I've been on a motorcycle wreck where an older couple (just married) died; I've looked for bodies thrown from cars in the woods. But I've also gone on calls to abandoned vehicles or people who were deeply asleep, but a family member thought they had died.

I've dealt with rape victims and murder victims, suicide victims, and suicide threats. But I've also come to houses with parents who simply couldn't get their disobedient children to go to bed, or homebound patients who wanted their feet raised.

I've cleaned blood, poop, pee, vomit, bone, sinew. I've made adjustments to fat rolls (at the patient's request only).

I've cut off clothes. And asked people to put on clothes.

I've seen children die. And children live.

I've gone on calls with rings of worried loved ones surrounding the dying. And I've gone on calls where people are punching one another, but no one will press charges.

I've watched choking and coding. But I've also carted perfectly healthy people to the hospital for reasons that don't seem to exist.

I've heard crying and wailing, moaning and heaving, cursing and praying, sighing and silence.

I've heard parents tell their children what to do; I've seen parents ask their children what to do.

I've seen filthy houses, beds with no sheets, children's feet caked in grime. I've walked under high ceilings and chandeliers.

For all this, a paycheck came. Twenty dollars to the hour. It's our goal to be on scene less than ten minutes and then drive to the hospital quicker than that. Which means that for every life I save, every life I watch ebb away, every mother who cusses at me, every elderly patient who enjoys a little midnight company, every shooting, stabbing, choking, heart attack, car accident, forgotten seatbelt, broken limb, diabetic crash, fainting spell, asthma attack, fever, stomach bug, wayward child, abusive partner, drug seeker, attention seeker, invalid, outpatient, old woman or man, (or young woman or man who thinks they're dying of an old person disease), every tuck into bed, every flatlined heart. For every part I hate or cherish. Every part that breaks my heart or heals it. Every patient who laughs or swears. Every call that irritates or fulfills me. For all of these, I earn about seven bucks.

Job done. Dust off my hands. Head back to the station or to my next call.

It's what I signed up for. A deal with a devil. A contract with an angel. I'm never sure.

It tears me. Sometimes it seals me.

Seven bucks.

The price of a soul. Or a double quarter pounder with cheese.

The Bad Samaritan
BY J.K. PACE

Once upon a time a couple scheduled a trip to Curacao for March 2020. We all know how that story ends. So they rescheduled it for the fall of 2020 because surely the pandemic would be forgotten history by then. Ahem. And then they scheduled it again for spring of 2021, at a time in which numbers were down almost everywhere in the world except . . . you guessed it, Curacao, where the beaches were still closed. But this couple had already arranged for Grandpa to fly out and watch the kids, so it seemed like maybe they should go *somewhere*.

And go somewhere they did. A darling bootstrap city filled with jazz and charm. A little place called New Orleans. Maybe you've heard of it. They booked a bed and breakfast, packed up bags and bikes (because surely you could bike around a city with a whole section called The French Quarter), and headed south.

A city of food, music, and alligators? What's not to love? Answer: Everything that isn't food, music, or alligators.

With all due respect to New Orleans, if it had to pick a

motto, it might be: The trashiest place you've ever gone on purpose.

The weather didn't help. It rained on and off, with full-on pouring all day Saturday. Those bikes stayed locked up tight (really tight, because cats aren't the only creatures who roam there at night). Though, rain or shine, it's not a city easily biked, especially the cute but narrow-streeted French Quarter. Truth be told, it's not a city easily driven either. We encountered barely a street that wasn't fully filled with potholes. In fact, one day we drove down a cobblestone road and James said, "You know, this is the least bumpy street we've driven on."

Truth.

But those potholes and that rain didn't keep us from the Cajun Adventure. It didn't keep us from seeing alligators, snakes, wild boars, and raccoons tame enough to apply to work for Disney. It didn't keep us from the beautiful garden district, the old trees, Spanish moss, cemeteries. It didn't keep us from the French Quarter either. Though I admit that I expected a little more quaint perfection and a lot fewer puddles and souvenirs made in China.

The food, however, was impressive, just like everyone said it would be. We didn't eat a single thing that wasn't delicious: from BBQ to beignets, from crawdads to ice cream, from Mufeletta sandwiches to something as basic as a plate of pasta.

We ate dinner Friday night on Bourbon Street—an iconic enough thing to do. It wasn't bad at first. Our food was delicious. An occasional street musician made his way out into the ruckus to dance or play drums. But neither of us drink, and after dinner the crowds were getting a little wild for our taste. Too much shouting, too much pressing, too much flesh, too much stink. And it wasn't just booze—cigarettes, cigars, marijuana, pee—an entire gambit of odors to choose from, none of which was an odor I wanted to choose from. I legit held my breath for large portions of our walk down the street. But no worries, we would spend a while exploring the rest of the French Quarter and then go back for a peaceful evening at our bed and breakfast.

Unfortunately, by the time we were ready to make our way to the car and head back, most of the streets in the French Quarter had gone dark. Personally, I was ready to take my chances with Jack the Ripper on one of the quieter streets, but James thought it would be wiser to head back down Bourbon Street which, while loud, was not filled with enough shadows to hide each and every potential mugger or murderer this side of the Mississippi.

Unfortunately for us, it *was* filled with a tremendous number of thoroughly altered people who—for the most part—were probably not making decisions they'd be proud of in the morning. And there, just a few blocks away from our car, a crowd of these drunken citizens had gathered around a thoroughly unconscious homeless man. Apparently, he'd been hit and was, indeed, bloody in the face. One of us—we'll call her the Bad Samaritan—thought he'd be just fine and wanted to ignore him and go straight to the car. The other one—we'll call him the Good Samaritan—thought they should lend a hand if possible. I won't tell you who was who, but when the Bad Samaritan grumbled about it, the Good Samaritan said, "Don't you think I should see if I can help?"

And what are you supposed to say to that? *No, let him rot in the gutter; let's go home and eat chocolates.* I mean, even Bad Samaritans can't say that out loud. And so, the Good Samaritan helped, which mostly involved keeping somewhat kindly drunk people from rolling the unconscious man around or trying to give him CPR even though he was breathing and his heart was beating just fine. All the while, the Bad Samaritan paced back and forth, trying not to gag because this was by far the stinkiest corner of the entire street.

Eventually, the injured man came to and sat up.

"Great," the Bad Samaritan thought. "Now we can blow this joint and I can go home and shower the stink out of my hair." But they were still waiting for an ambulance (which never came, incidentally; because this is New Orleans, darn it, not Mayville). And the man wobbled about and eventually stood and said he was okay and didn't need an ambulance anyway (the one time James—I mean the Good Samaritan—did touch him was when he almost fell backward while attempting to walk). And, I mean, he clearly wasn't okay, but it seemed like he might be as okay as he was going to be or maybe as okay as he usually was. At any rate, he was ready to move on and there was nothing more that we could do (and by 'we,' I mean the Good Samaritan, because that Bad one hadn't been doing much at all, except pacing from corner to corner with a rod up her butt).

"Are you mad at me?" the Good Samaritan asked as they made their way to the car.

And what was the Bad Samaritan to say? "No. I'm just kind of mad in general."

A true statement from someone who wasn't used to giving up a perfectly good evening to help someone out who hadn't done too much to help himself. A true statement from someone whose job didn't involve drunks, addicts, hookers, homeless people, or any combination thereof. A true statement from a life without a daily experience of blood or guts or head wounds, without the jaded kindness that allows you to crouch over a man with blood on his face and beer on his breath and dirt on his clothes, and say, "Hey, can you hear me? I'm here to help."

PART VI

Failing

One Sandwich

He has no legs.

From the upper thigh down. It's the first thing I take in as we go to him, unconscious on the floor by his bed. Not the best thing to see when you enter a scene. But his color is fine, his breath deep. The snake-like bulge of a fistula pops from his arm—the result of dialysis, and a sign of renal failure. He's sweating. A lot. Clearly, this is a problem with his blood sugar—concerning, but straightforward.

We test him, give him a whole amp of D50 (25 grams of sugar). His eyes move, opening, focusing. They go from 'nobody's home' to 'somebody's there.' His breath changes, faster as his mind surges out of a fog and he wakes up, sits up. It feels like a miracle, like a gone soul reunited and raised from the dead by the liquid equivalent of five lollipops.

And then he talks. No, he doesn't want to go to the hospital. Why would he want to go to the dern hospital when he's just fine? We don't make him. Now that he's alert and oriented, we couldn't even if we wanted to; and we don't. Diabetic patients are stressful and time-sensitive, but clear cut and easy to fix, or at least to patch up.

His family wanders in and out, relieved to see him talking. He rises to his leg stumps and hop-hops himself into his bed. Just like that.

I stare. Stumps just below the groin. No ankles, no knees, only an inch, maybe two, of actual leg. Yet, like some kind of cartoon character, he bounces his way up and into his bed. I'm impressed. At both his skill and his seeming recovery.

"You need to eat some food," I tell him, like I tell every other patient in his situation. "Sugar water won't last long."

He acts (and his family acts) as though he has every intention of complying with my advice. We check his blood sugar again. Rising steadily. Right on track. Normally, we wait until someone brings in a snack; normally we make sure the patient eats. But this time, we don't. That triumphant hop back into bed, that comfortable confidence in his condition—it feels like enough reassurance.

It shouldn't.

My partner calls me that morning as I'm driving home from work, tells me the news just as I pull into my driveway. Day shift had gotten the call after I left. Same address. Patient dead.

My partner is surprised. Me too.

I stare at my house, picturing the patient—alive then, dead now. I can't line it up. It should be easy. I've seen a lot of dead patients; I've seen even more who look dead. But this patient—he was alive. He hopped on two stumps into bed. I play it again in my mind.

No legs. Kidneys in renal failure. Obvious he didn't take care of himself. His family didn't either. No one did.

But we could have.

That small condemnation.

A mantra hammering in my head. *We could have.*

We could have monitored the blood sugar longer. We could have watched him eat. We could have, should have, known exactly the type of person who would not take our advice, would not follow the sugar water down with a sandwich or yogurt or anything at all.

In my field, one thing matters more than all the rest. It's not medicine or heartbeats or blood loss or hustle. It's not charting or blood pressures or fevers or flus.

It's knowing.

Knowing when something is dangerous or deadly, knowing when something needs extra care, time, speed. It's recognizing danger, even when others can't. In that room, with family members around, with an old man who could jump somehow from floor to bed, with protocols followed and paperwork in order, I lost sight of that danger, and left it to itself.

Then danger did as danger sometimes does. It went to sleep and didn't wake up.

The weight of that fail sits and cracks at places in my chest. It's a strange thing to think of losing a man—a man who didn't seem to care particularly about the depths of life, a man you technically saved who then went and lost himself—as your biggest failure, your hardest loss. And yet there he is, still hopping into the bed of my memory.

When I get up the courage to tell my wife, when I start on the story I don't want to tell, the one I consider my biggest failure, she holds up a hand, stops me. "Wait, he didn't have any *legs.*"

"Yeah," I say.

"So, he wasn't managing his diabetes at all?"

"No, not really. He was on dialysis too. For renal failure."

"Was he young?"

"No, not so much."

She sits back into the couch, looks at me, her pen motionless against the paper. "I'd expected a different story."

Maybe I had too. The loss of a child, a suicide, the failure of a heart we were trying to restart, too much or too little of a drug gone wrong. A million ways to die when you're nearly there anyway. But how can I tell her that with every other call, with every other death, with every other miss, they were outside of me—battles already fought and lost—things I had no real control over anyway. But this, this was one sandwich away from waking up in the morning. One sandwich away from a regular day. One sandwich away from seeing the sun. One danger I didn't see. One difference for good I didn't make.

A few pieces of bread I could have watched him eat.

But didn't.

Boy and "Man"

Regrets come in all shapes and sizes. Even in this business, when it seems they should only come in a sickness- or death-sized shape, they don't. Not always.

This call was for a behavioral issue, not a threat to self or anyone else, but a ten-year-old boy who was "out of control." He wasn't when we got there. They never are. By the time we arrived on scene, the police were there, talking to the parents—well, the mother anyway. The father was gone—had been for several years. Now replaced by a boyfriend—a thirty-something-year-old guy who smelled like cigarettes. The child came out from a back room, apprehensive, quiet, standing around like a normal kid would have been. Just a kid. A kid who knew he was in trouble.

The mother was in tears, saying, "I just don't know what to do."

But we don't come armed with parenting advice or counseling services. Our job is to figure out whether anyone needs to go to the hospital or not. The only "need" to go to the hospital in this case would be for a psych evaluation at the ER. Our small hospital didn't even offer that service, which meant we would have to take him across the state border to a larger hospital. Once there, the wait could span from one to seven hours, depending on how busy the ER was. Then the hospital would call a social worker if they felt the boy needed more of an evaluation. If the social worker decided the boy was a threat to himself or others (unlikely since that was not the case now), he would be admitted to a psych hospital for a seventy-two-hour hold. But if the social worker decided he was fine (the most likely scenario), then he would just go home.

Is that really what they wanted us to do? Send him to the ER to wait for hours?

When really all they needed—when all the patient (kid) and parent(s) usually need in this situation—is a minute. A minute to separate, a minute to cool off, a minute to be human again. Maybe even an hour. But not a call to police, not a drive to the hospital by ambulance, not a lengthy wait in a germ-filled emergency room.

The problem is that some parents (and even nursing home staff) often default to 911 to "fix" their out-of-control kids (or old people). And it's effective. Effective to call the police, to have a bunch of emergency vehicles show up outside your door. Most kids settle down pretty fast when that happens. So next time the kid loses it, the parent calls again. And again. As though we're the Bad Kid Babysitter's Club and the perfect solution to all these complicated family problems.

"I don't know what to do," the mom whimpered.

But she would have to be the one to decide. Since the child had made no threats to himself or anyone else, we couldn't just take him without parental consent.

A dangerous threat wasn't why we'd come. We had come for a kid who'd been tossed back and forth between parents, (one of whom was rumored to have a drug problem in the past, one of whom was rumored to be with a new wife, a new family, leaving old things behind—it was a small town, and we heard things). So now this boy in the middle of that had lost his temper, gone on a screaming, ranting rage, maybe throwing things, cursing, being aggressive. The details are a blur. That raging kid was gone now. All I could see was a scrawny little boy, subdued, any fury burned into shame. The mom and boyfriend now on their own rant—a laundry list of things he'd done wrong. Explaining to us and the police that this child didn't respect his mom, show any regard for authority, that he was out of hand, out of control, disobedient. And then the boyfriend —seeing that he had our ear, maybe wanting to show off his own superior parenting skills, turned to this little kid and said, "I know some kids who will be happy to take you out back and teach you some manners."

I'm sorry, what?

I was surprised the police didn't say anything. After all, you can't just threaten violence to another person. Especially some kid.

I remember looking at the cops, waiting.

Okay, we're just gonna let that slide, huh?

And the thing is, we did.

They did.

And I did.

So while I'm tallying regrets, let me add this to the list. I wish I'd turned to that man and said, "You can't say that to this child. You can't threaten to send your boys after him. It's illegal. And you're a jerk." (Technically, they had a lot more cause to take the boyfriend in than the boy. After all, a ten-year-old's tantrums aren't illegal. Threatening a child's safety is.) Truth be told, I wish that the next time the woman had blubbered that she just didn't know what to do, I'd said, "Start by getting a better boyfriend. Or maybe no boyfriend at all."

But I didn't. Kept my mouth shut. Waited for Mom's decision.

She wanted us to take the kid in for a psych eval.

So we did. Drove him across the state border, dropped him off at the hospital. Went back to work.

Regretted it ever since.

PART VII

Carrying

Part VI

Surveying

The Things They Carried

They carried walkers, canes, even wheelchairs to be crammed into a corner of the ambulance. They carried dirty blankets or pillows, stuck to the fluids of their bodies or kept around them for ease in transport.

They carried luggage—prepacked as they wait for us on the porch—the ambulance a cab to their favorite vacation.

They carried animals of all kinds, claiming the need for emotional support. (If they did not have official paperwork, they only carried them so far, because animals without paperwork would not get on the ambulance.)

They carried cell phones like babies. Newspapers, cigarettes, lighters, Juuls.

They carried cash if they were lucky. Coats, jackets, sweaters, shawls wrapped around old bodies.

They carried shoes they'd hunted as we were trying to leave—sometimes matching and sometimes not.

They carried garbage cans they'd been using to throw up in—cans we convinced them to replace with small vomit bags.

They carried sodas and burgers, nuggets and milk-shakes, things too precious to leave behind.

The homeless carried dirty bags filled with food or clothes or stacks of change. Life's possessions and life's stories wrapped into a package I wouldn't touch without gloves.

They carried onion rings and remote controls.

They carried medicines and empty bottles.

They carried stories of woe.

Pictures and memories.

Things they used to be. Things they still wanted to be.

They carried wishes for life.

They carried threats for death.

They carried smells.

Addictions. Withdrawals. Tears.

They carried loved one's names on moaning lips.

They carried curses. So many. For me, for them, for girlfriends, fathers, friends, enemies.

They carried wounds I could touch and wounds I couldn't.

They carried and carried and carried.

When they got into the ambulance, some let go of the things they carried. And many did not. Those we would see the next night or the next.

Carrying, as they do, the things we carry.

The Things We Carried

We carry a jump kit into every house. A world of modern-day witchcraft held in one hand. Items to save a life. Or determine one dead. With it, we carry breathing tubes, IV catheters, syringes, needles, bandages, tourniquets, oxygen masks, cannulas, and medicine. We carry nitro and aspirin, Adenosine and Cardizem, Albuterol and Atrovent. We carry D50 or D10, glucose and Narcan. We carry epinephrine, Atropine, Lidocaine, Amiodarone, sodium bicarbonate. We carry Zofran and Benadryl.

Things that stop blood; things that start hearts. Things that give breath; things that slow it. Sugars and salts. Medicines to stop allergies, nausea, overdoses, chest pain. Elixirs to make your heart beat faster, or slow it down. Things in needles; things in pills.

We carry airway kits with plastic tubes or long, broad needles like straws to be inserted into the throat. Small needles with valves that will let air out of collapsed lungs that can't release the building pressure. Needles for bones, needles for blood, needles for muscle.

A bag valve mask to hold over a mouth if we need to

breathe for them. Electricity to defibrillate into a heart that wants to beat.

Once back on the ambulance, we carry IV drips with bags of lidocaine and dopamine. We carry OB kits with sterile tools for tying and cutting cords, a small baby hat, and baby's first blanket, pulled from a sterile plastic casing. We carry blankets, sheets, pillows, splints, C-collars, flashlights, a backboard, and oxygen.

We carry mass casualty kits with the smallest, saddest things: a vest that says Medical Officer, paper for recording names, and four tags for victims. Black, dead. Red, critical. Yellow, stable with the potential to turn critical. Green, walking wounded.

We carry tools to organize as much as give life, for situations when giving life depends on a certain level of order.

We carry what we hope will bring life for times when life is slipping.

We carry our own hearts, our own hands. Wallets with cash, or credit card debt. Keys for the ambulance and the narcotics cabinet. Extra clothes to replace those with vomit, feces, or blood. We carry fear and cynicism. Hope and hurt. We carry annoyance—a whole lot of that. We carry arguments from the station, our last evaluation. We carry tired shoulders and aching backs. Some carry babies in their own wombs. Some carry problems from their own homes. Some carry secrets from their own lives.

We carry them up to your porch and into your home. And when we are done, we carry pieces of your pains and problems back to our own houses, our own people, our own lives. Sometimes we carry it heavy. Sometimes we carry it light. But we carry it.

Fetus

She holds the fetus in her hands, sitting on the toilet. The umbilical cord reaches, still connected, between her legs.

Attached, the baby breathes.

But I know it cannot stay connected outside of the uterus. And I know that once the cord is cut, the baby will die.

It is (or will be—such a foggy distinction at this point of barely-alive baby) the mother's fourth miscarriage, though I don't know if she's ever held the fetus, still living, in her hands. Sixteen weeks, she tells us, emotional, though helpful, guiding us to the information we need.

I check the mother, who is our official patient—the doomed baby not on the list. And then, to be as sure as I can be, I check the child. It opens its mouth. So small. The head, the hands, everything. I cannot even determine its gender. I cannot breathe for it. I cannot do anything to save the life that sits in a woman's hands.

The cord will need to be cut. The lifeline officially severed. The child's body is not developed enough to handle the support the NICU can give it. Still, cutting the cord is not an easy decision. I call the ER doctor, hoping against hope for . . . something—something miraculous, something impossible.

All the while the baby breathes. All the while, the mother quietly cries.

The doctor listens, confirms that a fetus of that age cannot be saved, and that it cannot—in a science fiction way—remain attached to its mother, carried around in some type of external, artificial womb, or neatly tucked back inside. He tells me to cut the child from its mother. He doesn't tell me in those words. He uses official ones like 'fetus' and 'patient.'

I clamp off the cord, take out a scalpel. Under the circumstances, it is necessary to do all of this basically in the mother's lap. I don't know if she watches or looks away. I pause. I am accustomed to attaching cables and tubes that give life, not taking them away. No matter how necessary. No matter that the baby's death is assured regardless of any of my actions; that I'm only speeding up an essential process and freeing the mother to proceed toward healing. No matter that the mother understands, accepts the reality of the situation.

I cut the cord. Hold the baby in my hand. The size of a newborn kitten. When I touch its hand, it moves slightly, living still.

My partner wraps the baby, releasing oxygen from the tube near its mouth while I finish assessing the mother. Then we take mother and child to the hospital where the baby lives beside her for a few more hours of the night.

We don't take life. And we don't give it. God and fate and science govern those choices, sometimes allowing us to extend life, sometimes to heal life, sometimes to withdraw it from the unsustainable supports that want to carry it.

Blurry lines of medicine.

Lines that are hard to see through tears. Mine, yours, a mother's whose fourth baby—a helpless wisp of a living thing—has died.

Wrestles, Again

Methampheteroids

The patient is bouncing around like a squirrel shot from a cannon. Talking too fast to finish his sentences, jumping around, legs and arms flailing without any real direction—kicking out at random times as though his nerves had mysteriously disconnected from his brainstem.

I don't remember how the call came in—anxiety, racing heart, shortness of breath. But it's pretty clear that he's flying high.

The patient is in his twenties, thick-muscled, and tall. Not our usual clientele.

"What have you taken today?" It's a question we always ask our patients, even if they're not high. It's information about medicine that can help us with treatment, that can save a life.

But the patient doesn't like the question. Immediately defensive, he blurts out, "It's probably that one of my meds was bad."

"What kind of medicine?"

He lists off a few medications.

I don't usually do this, because I don't usually care

enough to push myself on a jittery two-hundred-pound man, but today I ask, "Did you take any methamphetamines?"

The guy prickles. "I've never taken meth."

All the while, his legs are jerking out as though pulled by strings, arms whipping up and down.

"Look, just tell me."

He gets mad.

"It was just a bad medicine. Probably Medicine Z." (Note: Not an actual name.)

Again, I usually try to avoid aggravating potentially high patients, especially the big ones. But today the argument slips out of my mouth. "Never heard of it."

"Well, you're stupid."

It's been a while—years actually—since I've gotten touchy on a call. Patients are nasty all the time—name calling, arguing, resisting physically. Usually, they don't faze me anymore. Usually. Something about this one does.

"Why don't you just tell me you took meth?"

At this point, my partner is getting a little nervous, trying to send a nice message with his eyes: *Let it go.*

And why don't I? Instead, I ask again, "No meth?"

"Why you gotta be so stupid? If you knew anything you'd have heard of Medicine Z. It's a steroid medicine. It must have gone bad."

And I usually DO. NOT. CARE.. But there was something about this, something that cracked a little inside me, and I wanted to hear him say it. I wanted to hear him tell me: "You're here—tending to someone in the prime of life, someone who should be perfectly healthy—because I took crystal meth."

I didn't hear those words. A bit of self-preservation kicked in and I stopped pressing before getting myself punched in the face. We drove our high little (well, big) friend to the ER.

Incidentally, I've never heard of that drug since and when I asked the ER doctor that night, he'd never heard of it either. I've gone back to mostly not pushing my patients to talk when it's clear they're not going to. Although there are still nights when I want to hear it: "You're here, right now—not because of fate or bad luck or poor health—but because of something dumb that I did."

In the Custody of Strangers

If you're so drunk that you can't stand, you're not even allowed to go to jail.

Enter—not the boys in blue—but the men and women in, well, whatever color the EMS uniform is (mine is navy).

We arrive on scene, and we're generally greeted by five different types of drunk:

1. The combative drunk
2. The crying drunk
3. The injured drunk
4. The puking drunk
5. The peed himself drunk (also known as the currently-peeing drunk)

SO, basically, picture your nearest toddler, minus the cherubic cheeks and rewarding smiles. In lieu of those charming features, substitute some horrific breath, nasty body hair, ruined makeup and—generally—about 200 pounds.

Now you've got your patient.

And even though this patient cannot stand (much less walk), even though this patient cannot put together a coherent sentence, even though this patient may have a significant gash or sprain or broken bone (usually due to a fall), even though this patient likely has bodily fluids stuck in their hair, they will almost always not want to go with the friendly guys and gals who have arrived to help.

I've been spit on, peed on (not necessarily intentionally), insulted, cussed at, swung at (definitely intentionally—luckily most people have really poor aim when they can't see straight).

And yet we cannot leave them. To be clear, I don't mean this in an altruistic way. I don't mean we cannot leave them because we care so deeply and wouldn't want to abandon them while in this state. I mean, we literally are not allowed to leave them when they are not alert and oriented. In addition to bladder and leg control, they also lose the right to choose for themselves. This is called implied consent. It means that we are to assume that if they were in their right mind (they're not), they would want to come with us. It's the default for anyone who is unconscious, is a minor, has dementia, is unable to answer basic questions (name, date, where they are and what happened), threatens self-harm, or—of course—is too drunk to stand.

It becomes our job to try to gently coax these patients into coming. To try to reason with someone from whom reason (and other forms of self-control) has fled. To look someone in the eyes who's cussing up and down that they don't want to go, and to say, "You have to." To call a doctor if necessary to confirm. To call the cops if necessary to gain compliance (and a pair of handcuffs). To call the fire department if the patient can't walk or roll well enough to land on the cot, or if they weigh enough that we need more hands (big guys get drunk, too).

Sometimes it's a quiet drive. Sometimes they weep softly. Sometimes they swear and twist.

And it's hard—not just to deal with the antics—but it's hard to look another person in the eyes (however glazed or confused those eyes may be) and to say, "You've lost your right to refuse. You're coming."

This is even harder to say to an old woman with dementia. Or a suicidal teen. It's hard to look at a human being and say, "You are no longer a person with an array of choices. You are—temporarily—in the custody of strangers."

And, to be fair, we usually don't say it like that. We usually say, "Let's get you to the hospital so they can you get you fluids. Let's get you taken care of. Let's get you some place safe so you can sober up."

That is our job. To take people who are in danger, who are injured—whether it's inside or out—to a place where they'll be safe, where they can't hurt themselves (accidentally for the drunks, demented, or diabetics with too-low sugar, or on purpose for those who mean to do themselves harm).

But true or not, safety or not, potentially life-saving or not, I will never enjoy looking into the face of an unwilling person and saying, "You're going. You're going because you're too far gone."

PART IX

More Hard Laughter

The Night I Didn't Get Shot
(AND WHY YOU SHOULD HAVE AN
EASILY VISIBLE HOUSE NUMBER)

Standard call. Push button pendant. That meant that someone had fallen and famously couldn't get up. That, or they'd pushed it by accident. If I had to take a guess at a totally made-up statistic, I'd say that seventy percent of our push pendant calls were the latter. Sweet old folks who forget the instant 911 around their necks.

This one was in the country—not a whole lot of houses around, but not a whole lot of house numbers either (Public Service Announcement: If you plan to call 911 ever, or even get a hot pizza dropped off at the right time, invest in some nice, big, easy-to-see house numbers).

With that public service announcement ringing in your heads, imagine us winding our way down a country lane, looking for a house without numbers. It's the middle of the night—dark and starry or dark and stormy, I can't remember. But dark. It's probably about two in the morning at this point. We find one house number that's close and make the assumption that our spot is the next house over. (Assumptions on country roads are bad ideas.)

We knock on the door. We don't expect anyone to

answer since this is a call where the patient is likely on the floor unable to get up, but we want them to know we're here. "Hello," we call out, opening the unlocked door. "Paramedics here."

No response. Not great, but not completely unusual either. As medics we enter a lot of houses that aren't our own. We don't have to have permission or warrants. If we've gotten a call from a presumably distressed person, we just go in. And if the door is locked, then we look for a window. And if all of those are locked, we bust down a door or find another way to break in. All in a day's work.

"Hello," we call out again. "Can you tell us where you are?"

Nothing.

We walk through the living room, medical bag in hand.

And then a person wanders into the open, wearing a robe and looking bewildered and terrified. Suddenly, we're a little scared too. Remember, this is the rural south in the middle of the night. Gun country. We're wearing dark outfits and carrying a duffle-like bag, looking guilty in the middle of someone's living room.

"Did you call 911?" we say before anyone can draw a weapon.

Nope. She sure hadn't.

We leave with apologies, resume our house hunt and eventually find the right house with the correct "patient." Accidental call. (Told you. Seventy percent.)

Back to the station, glad we found the right house. Back to the station, glad we gave that wrong-address-woman a good story to tell her bridge club. Back to the station, glad we didn't get ourselves shot.

But for real, folks: Put numbers on your houses.

Lost In Translation

Often, my job goes a little like this:

DISPATCH: Something that sounds so horrible that it'll make the nightly news.

Translation: Something that will definitely not make the nightly news.

LET me show you what I mean.

DISPATCH: 19-year-old with chest pain.

Translation: He just got dumped by his girlfriend.

DISPATCH: Gunshot wound to the back

Translation: Acne (Yup, back-ne)

. . .

DISPATCH: Car accident
  Translation: Scratch on car

DISPATCH: Car accident
  Translation: Empty vehicle abandoned by the road

DISPATCH: Motor vehicle accident at assisted living.
  Translation: Wheelchair accident in assisted living.

DISPATCH: Lift Assist
  Translation: Snacks too far away to reach; please bring them closer.

DISPATCH: Lift Assist
  Translation: Full on crazy lady. Talks about part of her skull being removed. Insists we be careful not to "hurt her brain," aka touch her head.

DISPATCH: Lift Assist
  Translation: Vacuum cord wrapped on wheelchair.

DISPATCH: Lift Assist
  Translation: Remove patient's clothing so he can go to bed.

DISPATCH: Lift Assist
  Translation: Pooped self, please change.

. . .

DISPATCH: Unresponsive
    Translation: Sleeping

DISPATCH: Unresponsive
    Translation: Drunk

DISPATCH: Unresponsive
    Translation: Person vomiting and not responding to family when they ask if they're okay.

AND IT'S good to know, in its own weird way, that sometimes it's horrible, but usually, it's not.

When Things Go Wrong

Things go wrong. Most of them not our fault. It's the nature of a job in which people are constantly on the brink of disaster and, sometimes, well past the brink. It's the nature of a job in which you're relying on vehicles and equipment and other human people. The nature of a job in which you've never seen this exact situation ever before, never driven down this country road, never been in this house, never climbed these stairs. And you've definitely never touched this body—the one that now lies unconscious before you. You know nothing of this person's medical history, dietary habits, or moods. You know nothing at all except what a monitor or a sobbing family member can tell you. You know nothing but the moment—that one vital, disastrous snapshot of an instant when you arrive in a situation that is quickly spiraling downward. That moment. It is the nature of a job in which you must work quickly, each second counting, each minute dangerous.

It is the nature of a job in which at least half your work happens in the dark middle of night. The nature of a job that sometimes relies on volunteer firefighters to provide extra hands—extra hands that might be far away when the call comes out, that might not be able to get to your position to help you in time, or perhaps at all.

It is the nature of a job in which adapting to things is just as important as knowing things—sometimes more important. When I first began training as a new paramedic and was getting a lecture from the education director, I tried to defend myself, saying I just didn't have enough experience. She said, "Sometimes you don't know what you're doing. Sometimes it's a matter of improvising." (So let those words ring in your ear the next time you dial 911.) It's true. Improvisation is something we need to be just as good at as getting an IV or intubating or shocking a dying heart. Because sometimes you can't get the IV or the tube, and the shock doesn't do any good. What then?

It's a question most of us have answered hundreds of times.

We answer it each time only two people show up to a four-hundred-pound patient in cardiac arrest. The fire department or another crew might be on their way. But they're not here now, and that patient needs to somehow get into our ambulance.

We answer it when the batteries are low on the cardiac monitor—a monitor we really need to last all the way to the hospital because if we have a cardiac patient, we need to know what the heart is doing.

We answer it when the gas tanks (sometimes there are two) in the ambulance malfunction, showing that they are both empty, even though we just got a call and we're almost positive that one is full.

We answer it when a psych patient wiggles out of his restraints.

We answer it when we forget the cot at the ER (I didn't

say it was *never* our fault) and find ourselves with only a backboard to use on the patient.

We answer it when a man's femur is stuck in his car door (a reverse impalement—it's much more common for us to get patients with metal stuck in them, rather than one who has part of himself stuck through a metal object). Will we leave him there to suffer and die? Nope. Somehow, in some way, we'll free the femur from the metal of the door. If we have to, we'll cut the metal itself, releasing him. If we have to, I suppose we would even take the car door off and transport it with us (fortunately we've never had to).

I answered it the night I tripped on a brick entryway, lacerating my own knee. This happened on a serious call with a serious patient—a man who had fluid in his lungs and was struggling to breathe.

It was a call that started out straightforwardly enough. Not complicated, but very time-sensitive. When patients are truly struggling to breathe, we have to get them to the hospital as quickly as possible, preferably before they stop breathing altogether. However, despite this urgency, we can't hustle or hurry the patients. In fact, we have to do everything we can to get them on the ambulance with as little exertion on their part as possible.

We had the equipment to do this. I just had to get it out of the ambulance.

Simple, right? To get the patient down the stairs, we needed our stair chair. It's like a moving dolly, except that it's a chair patients can sit on. It also has wheels on the back that move smoothly down stairs. And I knew just where it was.

Four in the morning, dark, hilly. I thought the entryway was flat, flush with the grass. In reality it was raised a few inches. I plowed forward and missed the small step. My foot hit the edge, leaving my knee to catch me as I fell on the bricks. I knew I'd cut it, could feel the stinging pain, the sticky blood. It didn't matter. I hauled the stair chair up, and we got the patient to the hospital. Ten minutes, thank you very much. A flurry of nurses helping him. And then one for me. When we pulled up my pant leg to look at my knee, it turned out to be not just a scrape, but a deep laceration, flaps of skin in a surprisingly neat right angle.

I finished my paperwork that morning in the ER as a patient—getting my own wound stitched up by one of the doctors.

Things go wrong. We try to fix them. Sometimes we succeed; sometimes we fail. All I know is it's a lucky night when the worst thing that happens lands me a night off, with pay.

Dropping the Dead

Sometimes they're dead before we get there. Not stiff, gray dead, but not-going-to-recover dead.

The problem is that often they have a few electrical pulses buzzing through that heart of theirs. Which means we work them. Not with a tremendous amount of faith or hope maybe, but with a fair measure of charity.

This guy was one of those patients. Not really alive. But not yet flatline dead. And so, it became our job to work him. He did not improve. In fact, he became—if such a thing is possible—a little more dead. But he hadn't been down long and so we decided to take him to the hospital.

In cases like this we generally use a cot that has a sleeve with Velcro fastenings to hold the patient on as we take him from his home.

Unfortunately, this particular house had a sharp corner out into the hall.

We've got a six-foot backboard with a heavy patient, one who is well past the point of being able to help with his own weight, being technically dead and all. We've only got two guys since no other crews have yet arrived. And we've got a tight, narrow turn. In other words, we've got a problem.

Don't worry. Simple solution. We tilt the backboard like one might a couch. The patient is strapped in (and for all practical purposes, dead, so he won't care).

We tilt, one of us out of the room, one still in, and we hear a sound like tearing, although it's not tearing. Rather, it's the sound of Velcro detaching. Something you hear before you see. Something that slows down when you do see it. The body tipping forward off the backboard, the patient's wife in the hall, the grab and shuffle as we try to stop it from happening.

Our patient does not crash to the ground. He sort of crumples like a blanket unfolding. His wife does not—through some superhuman level of restraint—scream or swear at us. We bend down, put him back on—this dead man—re-fasten him, make the tilt, make the turn, get him on a cot, drive him to the hospital where he is declared solidly gone.

A patient past healing. An equipment malfunction. A moment of humanness and error and imperfection. That split-second look of horror between partners, that strange connection in a moment when nothing could be done, and things went down from there. That moment. They're a whole lot better than moments where something could be done, and things went down from there. A whole lot.

And as paramedics and partners, as friends and work buddies, we hold these things a little close, talk about them in years to come over dinner with spouses. Remember that time—that crazy time, that not-quite-good-day that wasn't the worst.

I like to think, in some of those moments, that some of

those dead guys are looking down from their place in the clouds—much better than that place they were when I last saw them—and laughing too.

PART X

Second Chances

Second Choices

The Man Who Lived

Usually, they die.

At least when they have good reason for dying, which he does.

In my twenty plus years of working in EMS, I've heard of fewer than ten people who have survived a cardiac arrest (after defibrillation) and gone on to live a meaningful life (not just a few brain-dead days at the hospital). Of my own patients, I know of only three such patients who have survived.

Three. Out of hundreds.

This patient is seventy-ish years old, unresponsive, with erratic breathing. It's not the type of report that gives any EMS crew a lot of hope when dispatch sends in the call. *Guess it was his time to go.* It's what we're all thinking as we throw on jackets, clamber into the ambulance, and head out.

By the time we arrive, he's no longer breathing, but only recently down. Even more importantly, his heart still quivers in V-Fib, trying to live.

We shock him. Twice. And in one of those rare movie

moments, he comes back. Oh, he doesn't hop off the cot and start talking or run after criminals or anything like that. But his heart rate returns, his blood pulses. I tube him and, as the blood continues to pump, he begins to resist the tube too. During our drive to the ER, he's moving around, attempting to remove the tube from his throat. Fighting a tube after being medically dead is a very good thing.

Once at the ER, he's breathing well enough to have the tube taken out. He talks. He responds to questions. His heart lives. His brain lives.

We go back into the night. We often go back into the night, which sounds cool and Batman-esque, but is usually just tired and often sad. Tonight we float. We talk. We replay the scene with happiness instead of regret.

Still, we never expect to see that man again. Never expect him to call our office, find out what station we work at, and come out to meet us personally. And yet, about a month later, he shows up with gift cards and tears.

Seventy years old, but recently married. Ready still for so much life. Which we gave him. Or at least allowed him to keep.

One life among billions.

One save among thousands.

"I can't ever thank or repay you," he says, "but I want you to know how grateful I am for saving my life."

Life. It's not something we ever promise, barely hope for, often lose. It's something paramedics spend most of our training learning to preserve, only to fail most of the time.

It's something that stands before us now, beaming.

One life. We're all grateful for it.

Death and Life, Lost and Found

It's one of my first intubations. I don't succeed.

The patient, an older asthmatic woman—is struggling to breathe, her lungs swelling and closing. The paramedic who is training me leans over my shoulder. It seems that the tube has entered the patient's esophagus instead of her airway, though—to be honest—neither of us is completely sure. "Pull it out," he says.

I do, and try again, but I don't get it this time either.

My trainer instructs, gives advice. I try again and again, failing each time as the patient's breath grows thinner, lungs swell thicker.

Two other paramedics are on the scene with me—my trainer and partner. Neither shoves me out of the way, takes over. I wish they would. This woman is dying under my fingers, and I don't know how to stop it.

Looking back, I'm not sure why they didn't interfere. Looking back, I hunt for reasons.

Did they think we would save her regardless? (Possibly.)

Did they believe she would die no matter what, so they didn't try? (Unlikely.)

Did they not believe any of us would be able to get the tube due to her already constricted lungs and throat, so they allowed me to keep trying? Did they feel they couldn't have done any better? (Seems impossible, but why else not take the stupid tube and do it themselves?)

Did they believe we could bag her later and that the lost time wouldn't matter? (Feasible.)

Did they—on some subconscious level—know we were going to fail and want me to do it instead of them? (Jaded me feels this is a good possibility; other me questions my cynicism.)

Regardless of their reasons, they did not interfere, did not take the tube, did not do it themselves.

Fifteen years (and hundreds of intubations) later, I like to think I would have known if I'd done the tube right, would have known if I'd hit the esophagus or trachea, would have felt confident about it.

Back then, I didn't know anything. Except maybe how much I didn't know, how much I should know, how insufficient I seemed to be on every single call. It wasn't a field that tolerated a whole lot of screw-ups, and I already doubted my place in this world of emergency medicine.

That day, we rushed a dying woman to the hospital. En route, the other paramedic finally got the tube. But it was too late. The patient had retained too much carbon dioxide because she didn't have an adequate airway.

And so, a woman, sixty years old, died of asthma. Which is stupid. A waste. A loss.

I felt the shame of that loss for months: replaying, rewriting, reworking. None of this changed the outcome. A woman was gone.

I feel the need here to point out that nothing we did on the call was "wrong" or against protocol. In fact, at times

I've wondered if that was the problem—our team following all the steps, all the rules, nothing wavering.

The call threw me. The job threw me. Soon—although it was less straightforward than that—I quit. I wandered for a month, doing odd jobs, hoping to stumble into something wonderful and long-term, and wondering why I'd gotten into this career in the first place. Money dwindling, parent of a newborn, and with my wife in graduate school, I took a job working with disabled adults, earning less than ten dollars an hour. It didn't take long to realize that—whether I wanted to or not—I would have to give my chosen field another shot in order to support my young family. Within a month I took a different job, forty-five minutes up north, working for a busier and less prestigious company.

We ran a lot of calls. I learned a lot of things—not from a trainer, but from cold, hard necessity. Within a year of working with them, we encountered another asthma patient—this one a seven-year-old boy.

We got to his trailer, found him sitting on the couch, struggling to breathe. Within five seconds, he had slumped over, unconscious. Dying.

The biggest thing you need in a pediatric code is an airway. If you can fix that, you can fix almost anything. A heart—even a perfectly healthy heart—will stop if the breathing stops for too long. You grant air; you grant life.

We granted air. We put him on the floor, and I had my partner bag him while I prepared the tube. For a few moments we breathed for him, pushing air into his lungs through the bag. But I knew we still needed to succeed with the intubation. At this point, I was both more skilled and more confident in my work, but even more importantly, I knew I would do anything to keep this kid from dying. In a movie-esque moment, I stopped caring about rules and protocols. I knew I would do what I had to. Even if it was "wrong," even if I broke protocol. Even if it cost me my license or career or a lawsuit. Interestingly (and very non-movie-esque), I did not *need* to break any rules; I did not need to sacrifice my career for a life. I just needed to know that I could, that I would—that the patient, the boy, mattered more than my own fears of failure, than my own insecurities. In that choice, my mind freed, my skill level soared—knowledge and understanding and months of practice available for me to access without my dread of failure to tamp them down.

I got the tube.

And then, beautifully, the boy began breathing for himself. He was still not conscious, but he was breathing. By the time we got to the hospital, he was coming to, moving, waking, living.

Once we'd gotten him to the ER, I walked through the waiting room, passing his father. I looked at him, knowing how close he had come to losing his son.

And in that moment, I knew I was found—the months of confusion and sadness, of struggle and learning. All worth it.

A child saved.

A piece of me too.

Noise and Silences

One of my first calls as a new EMT lands me on a playground where a little girl has fallen. A tumble from the monkey bars. Possible broken arm. Not really an emergency, and definitely not exciting. I want to see shootings and heart attacks, blood loss and concussions. I want to help people who "really need" it.

As we load the little girl into the ambulance (or tell her parents just to take her to the ER—I honestly can't remember how it played out), a group of police cars, firetrucks, and ambulances tear through the streets, sirens screaming. Something is going on downtown. Something loud. Something big. Something I want to be a part of so much more than a weepy little girl.

In August of 1999, I get that call. A tornado has ripped through an outdoor event in a large western city, killing one and injuring dozens of people. Over twenty units show up to calm and aid the terrified masses. TV crews with cameras, coverage that makes the national news. Noise, presence. That night on TV, I watch myself from a bird's eye view, walking the scene. I still don't feel that I've made a difference. I haven't. The man who died couldn't be saved, and most of the other patients were bruised or scratched, maybe a few broken bones. No superhero cape for me. No badge of honor. No running around, shouting to my crew, "Go, go, go." And if I had been running around, shouting "Go, go, go," hopefully the cops would have arrested me then, and put me out of my misery. No matter the call, people need calm; they need knowledge; they need efficiency. Men in tights need not apply. But was that what I wanted to be? Some type of hero? A white knight or a dark knight or any knight at all, someone excessively buff with a logo on his chest? Someone who would save the world and have them know it?

Fast forward twenty years. Another city. Another state. Another call. I've gone to more school, gotten more certifications, become a paramedic. Husband, father too. I've seen blood, bone, corpses, bar fights, guts, gunshots, knife wounds, abuse, vomit, and more poop than any sane person could ever imagine.

And then, on a night like every other night, we get a guy. With a bullet in his neck. He is still alive. Still breathing. Still sitting up. But we can see it there, lodged under the skin. He'd gotten in a fight with someone over a girl or something like that. He'd been shot in the shoulder, where the bullet had entered, then *exited*, striking his neck. After that, the bullet had travelled (miraculously) through one side of his neck to the other, where it lodged, just under the skin. After getting shot, he'd made his way to a friend's house.

The friend is with him now; the sheriff too.

The patient has wounds to the shoulder and neck, but only a trickle of blood—no gushing.

"Is he going to live?" his friend asks. A fair question, without an answer. He should already be dead.

The patient tells me it hurts to talk.

"Then don't talk," I say, still stunned that he has an airway and can speak at all. And he's not bleeding out— our two biggest concerns. These are also things that could change at any minute with any movement. One wrong turn or nod or twitch, and he could dislodge the bullet, causing more damage or letting the damage done break free in a sea of unblocked blood.

It's a quiet scene. Eerie almost. No screaming. No crying. Very little talking. We try to get a helicopter, but none are available. So we help him to a cot. Just like we would a granny or a diabetic. No camera crews wait outside, no reporter asks questions at a furious pace. We drive to the hospital. A team of nurses and surgeons take it from there, removing the bullet from near the artery. Not long afterwards, a man who should have died goes home.

Maybe it makes the local paper, but no one mentions it if it does.

A few weeks after that, we go on another gunshot. This one self-inflicted, through the chest. A man trying, suppos-edly, to avoid being deployed. Though he was quite heavy and—we later learn—not in the military. Story, delusion, drugs or drink, paranoia, mental illness, fake news of an upcoming draft. Who knows? Whatever the reason, he now has a hole in his torso. Entrance wound, exit wound, blood and guts. The works.

He is kneeling on the floor, still conscious when we arrive. "That was stupid," he says.

No room for argument there, but knowing that doesn't help now. I start two IVs just in case he starts bleeding too much and bandage him front and back, hooking him up to the monitor to watch his heart. We get him onto the cot, and off to the hospital he goes.

Nobody shows up on a magazine cover (not him, not

us, not even the surgeon). Nobody makes a fuss. It's one story of thousands like it. In this case, I do not even learn if he lives or dies. Time passes as time does. Quietly, without fanfare for the hours and days that roll out from under us.

Several weeks later, we find ourselves at a restaurant, late at night, hungry and tired. The manager comes out, gives us a discount, and thanks us. Not for our work in general. But for saving her son. That guy who put a bullet through his chest. It's not a cover story, not a medal, not a crowd. It's fifty percent off a chicken sandwich and a few kind words. And it's nice. Nicer than I expect it to be. Nice to know what happened. Nice to know he lived. Nice to remember that even in the silences, maybe especially in the silences, these things still matter to someone.

Walk, Don't Run

Astronauts take leaps for mankind.
  Firefighters hustle up the stairs.
  Cops chase the bad guys.
  We walk.

PEOPLE DON'T WANT us to. They want us to run, to rush, to hurry.

But in our field: "Slow is steady. Steady is fast."

If you hurry, you screw stuff up and take longer. Even more importantly, if we run, *you* panic. And, even more importantly, if we run, it's because we're panicked. And panic kills.

An elderly man, disabled, living with family. A big hunk of his dinner stuck in his throat.

By the time we arrive he is unconscious. You might think that this is an exception, that we should run now. We don't. We walk. We think. We give clear instructions to a team that has a whole lot to do to save one man.

First, we have to get the patient to a place that we can

work him easily. Patients have a pesky habit of collapsing in the most inconvenient locations: by the toilet or crammed up against the dresser or halfway under the kitchen table (which is the case with this man). We drag him to a clear spot in the room.

I take the head. It's my job to remove the hunk of food from his throat. I can see it, which means that I can use Magill forceps to pull it out. This is lucky. But it is one step among many. While I'm using forceps to remove food from an unresponsive man's throat, the firefighters on scene begin chest compressions. This keeps blood flowing through the body, which means that there's less injury to the brain once (if) we can get the air flowing again. While they pump his heart and I dig food from his throat, the EMT prepares the IV. He gets the bag connected to the tubing, ready for me to start the IV once the airway is secure.

It's a rhythm, a symphony; and you can't have one of the instruments rushing forward, or the whole group will lose the beat. You can't have someone yelling, "I need that IV yesterday." You can't have someone trying to carry the patient out while another person is trying to remove food. In some choking cases, I've even had to ask the firefighters to stop chest compressions because it's moving the head too much for me to work. And they do stop—for a few important moments of stillness. Without an airway, all the chest compressions in the world will not save the man.

Tonight, we get the airway, which means that the heart could start pumping on its own (we hope it does soon), but there's still a ways to go before the man is saved. Since he is still not alert and oriented, I need to insert a tube into his throat in order to maintain the airway. This allows us to help him until he begins breathing on his own. (Or so we can bag him if he stops breathing after he's begun.) Then the IV goes in.

And often, so often, we're in a small space with a big patient. We need to move that big patient through a narrow doorway—one our cot usually won't fit through. During a code, we're trying to orchestrate getting a patient out the door, all while trying to maneuver around a variety of obstacles—shoes, couches, clocks, hutches, rugs, stairs. All without stopping CPR for too long. In order to make this happen, we lay out the backboard (smaller and more portable than a cot), then logroll him on. We tip the patient to the side, put the backboard behind him, then tip him back and strap him on. Together, we lift the patient and carry him through the doorway to the waiting cot. Even as we're rolling him onto the board, we're pumping air into his lungs, then doing chest compressions. We coordinate that slip through the door—those seconds when oxygen will stop yet again, as our team walks the patient through the door and lifts him onto the cot. Then it all begins again —bagging air into his lungs, compressing the heart as we move the cot down the hallway and through the front door (with any luck avoiding any staircases).

Into the ambulance and to the hospital.

Walking our way through the process. As the patient's heart finds its own rhythm, as alertness returns, as his breath flows more naturally through a throat that works all on its own. As the patient begins—also slowly, also steadily —his own walk back to the land of the living.

Dropping the Dead, Reprise

I don't remember the cause of such a young heart going out, but this guy was only thirty or forty years old. Often at that age, it's an overdose, though I can't say that that was the reason here. We arrived on scene. One ambulance and then another. All of us surprised, but still not hopeful, to find his heart in a shockable rhythm, quivering away. We shocked him. Once, twice. Again. And again. More than I usually shock a patient. But what did we have to lose? He was dying. He was, by certain definitions, already dead.

And so, we shocked. Past the charm of the third time, onto a fourth, maybe a fifth. So many times. And then his heart came back. Beating a rhythm, trying to live. Our hopes didn't soar. Our expectations didn't thump along with that desperate heart. But we did have, to all of our surprise (please note my restraint in not using the phrase 'to all of our shock' and making a pun here), a viable patient.

Onto the backboard and ready to face another opponent to our patient's survival: stairs.

Carpeted, split-level stairs. A single backboard, a large

patient, and four EMS workers—two big and two small. My memory of this event isn't perfect, but I'm pretty sure the smaller guys (one of those is me) took the feet position. The big ones, the head. Stepping together like a clumsy marching band. One step, then another, our bodies squeezed tight against the walls. One of us must have been bagging him—pushing air into his lungs with one hand, holding the corner of the backboard with the other. And then one of us slipped. I think it was a foot person. The edge of the cot dipped, and he almost went down; we almost went down. Four living guys and a mostly dead patient tumbling like dominoes to the bottom of the stairs. Almost. The grunts and pulls as we righted the board, hauling our trying-to-not-be-dead patient back up, finding our footing. Four deep breaths. Our own rhythm. Down the remainder of those steps. Out the door, into the ambulance.

He still wasn't responsive when we got to the ER. Which didn't bode well. Even if his heart lived, his brain would likely die, and then it was just a matter of time before they pulled the plug. Another day, another death. Another lost soul to add to our collection.

Which is why it was such a surprise when he showed up at the station a few weeks later with cookies. He'd done the entire round: ER, Fire, EMS. Thanking us all for saving his life. Living proof of second chances—the edge of a hope caught and righted.

PART XI

Finding Humanity

Miss Madeline

There are days. Days when we're not too happy about the calls we have to go on. Sometimes we handle it graciously. Sometimes we don't.

It's not uncommon to hear a door slam at the station when a call comes in. Streams of cussing. A ride full of complaint, bad mouthing the patient. "I'm so sick of so and so." Yes, we know a lot of them by name. Often we've been on the exact same call with the exact same person the night before; sometimes only a few hours before. We call them *frequent fliers*, these people who call night after night— usually (I would say 'always,' but I suppose there's an exception somewhere to prove the rule) with no significant medical needs. In general, these people are not, to put it sweetly, greatly adored by the emergency community.

Yet, despite the storms that sometimes follow a "frequent flier" call, there are moments of grace, people who can handle the calls with kindness. And plenty of days that demand it if you're going to survive in this field.

When the tones wake us up, dispatch crackles out a

familiar address. A female patient, lift assist. That would be Madeline. And the 'lift assist,' well, that could be anything from retrieving a cola from the fridge to lifting a limb dangling over the bed to a full-on diaper explosion. In other words, nothing we are super stoked about.

We throw on our boots and grab the keys.

When we arrive, Brad—one of the grace-filled medics —walks in with a smile. "Hello, Miss Madeline. How are you doing tonight?"

They chat. We fill up her soda, maybe make her more comfortable. She never wants to go to the hospital and so we get a refusal and head back to the station. That was an easy one.

But there are days, other days. Days when her at-home help doesn't show up, leaving Madeline—bed-bound and immobile—helpless for the entire day. On those days, we arrive to find her covered in poop or sitting on sheets soaked with urine. On those days we help the best we can. We aren't the only ones to help either. Day shift is no stranger to overburdened diapers in an overburdened system.

On one of those days (nights if we're being exact), the tones come on again, the familiar address. Only tonight we walk in to find Madeline lying in a pool of vomit and other excrement in the middle of her bed—so much worse than usual—my nose burning from the smell, my throat thick with a swallowed gag. I can't remember if Brad asks how her day was—it seems pretty obvious that it hasn't been the best. Her aide didn't show up for her shift (a shockingly common occurrence in a field that is even more under-valued and underpaid than our own—if you pay people $8/hour to do some of the dirtiest work around, you're not going to get the most reliable work force. I'm not excusing the no-shows, just making an observation).

Madeline has soiled her bed, overfilled her diaper (we're talking a good twenty-four hours' worth of waste), and finally thrown up. Maybe more than once. But Madeline doesn't want to go to the hospital.

Remember that it is our job to transport her and treat her along the way, nothing further. We could have gotten a refusal and left. None of our protocols required us to stay, to help in any way.

But we look at her lying there in a bed of her own fluids and I think (in an epiphany Brad must have hit on years ago), "This is a human being. We can't leave her like this."

And we don't.

Madeline is not a small woman—her immobility is due to her extreme weight. She never leaves her bed. She can't.

We start with the sheets. One of us rolls her to her side while the other rolls up that half of the dirty sheet, then scoots a clean one onto that part of the bed. When it is well enough in place, we roll her onto it, pushing her to her other side so we can pull out the remainder of the dirty sheet (rolling that sheet up the whole time so nothing falls out). Fortunately, Madeline sleeps on a hospital mattress, which repels water.

Sheet done, it's time for a day's worth of overfull adult diaper. We approach it with a similar method. Unfasten, then roll as we scoot the new diaper under, wiping the bottom as we go. Madeline's bum has considerably more surface area than a baby's and we do our best.

In a final feat of grace, we help her change from her dirty nightgown into a fresh one.

When we leave, it is with a clean patient on a clean sheet.

"You take care of yourself, Miss Madeline," Brad says as we walk out the door. Knowing we might be back the next night, or the next. Knowing it isn't our job to do this sort of thing. But knowing we will probably do it anyway. And finding—once we get past the frustration of that fact —a strange kind of peace in the knowing of it.

On Living When You Fear to
Die, COVID-19

Note: While this is Jean's essay, I stole James's experiences to write it. His experiences shaped my thoughts and formed the base for this essay. Call it a marital collaboration—his experiences wrapped into my words.

WE KNEW COVID-19 would bring with it a few casualties. It's what made us stockpile masks, hoard hand sanitizer, and endlessly scroll through our phones for the next news story, outbreak, statistic.

After all, none of us wanted to be a casualty.

It's what brought us together at first. And what tore us apart just weeks later when opinions and politics scratched their lines in the sand, deeper with every article and counter argument. Nowhere was it easier to see than in the charged issue of face masks. A sentence, which—if I'd written it in 2018—would have sounded so ridiculous that any novelist would have swiftly deleted it. And yet here we are—stranger, as usual, than fiction. Harder to edit too. Through COVID, some came to believe mask-wearing was

153

the solution, while others decided that masks themselves were a greater disease.

Mobs gathered, not in the streets, but on their couches —one group ready to verbally lynch the dissidents in their "friend" groups, while others mounted counterattacks through their 280-character buckets of tar and feathers.

The goal, after all, was survival, all of us fighting against death, all of us fighting—we said—to live. A worthy end. Justifiable by oh-so-many means. So what if we brought down a few friends or neighbors in the process?

Suicide rates rose, domestic violence, stress levels, unrest.

We fought death so hard from our living rooms and Twitter accounts that we forgot a little what it actually looks like, how regularly and ceaselessly it strikes. And how weak Facebook is to stand against it.

People walked into emergency rooms so terrified of COVID that they found relief in a diagnosis of cancer or heart failure. A relief that was often short-lived as death leveled her ax and swung.

And so we hunted—as humans do—for control over death. We tightened the reins on whatever issue we'd chosen to be our savior, and we cast heavy phrases like stones from a sling against any who opposed us.

If you don't wear a mask, you're basically killing someone's grandmother, said people from their recliners, who'd never seen a dead body, known a COVID patient, or stepped into a nursing home.

Well, if you make me wear a mask, you're robbing me of my basic human rights and freedoms—and that's death too, said people who could afford enough food to grow obese, own an armory that could kill a small village, and raise a child in any religion they chose.

Being right or wrong started to feel important—like

something that could control a situation, something that could maybe even stop it. If a person could be right enough loudly enough, then things—we told ourselves—would get better.

And certainly, sometimes being right can halt death. And certainly, sometimes being wrong can hasten it. But sometimes death comes when it comes. And believing that your own rightness (which morphs so quickly into righteousness) can save a person is the type of paving stone that marks a careful path to places good intentions often lead.

The truth is that most people have not seen death or the points leading up to it quite as much as those in the healthcare field—paramedics and EMTs, nurses, ER docs and nursing home staff. And the truth is that, when you have seen a lot of death, and when it is your job to stave it off whenever possible, you come to respect it. You know that death takes what it takes. And you know that to put a death onto another human's shoulders is not something a person should do lightly.

You know that wearing a mask will neither save nor destroy any more than shocking a dying heart or getting an unconscious diabetic's blood sugar up or finding an airway on a patient who is struggling to breathe. They might help; we hope that they do. But saving or killing are both labels too heavy to bear. Even with the best equipment, even with as much knowledge as you can hold.

And those things you can hold—they might aid, protect, filter, shield.

But masks or hand sanitizer or isolation will not be our end-all in the fight against death. Not any more than antibiotics or defibrillators or stints.

Often they help; sometimes they don't.

But remember this—whatever you do, whether you stay home or not; whether you mask up or not; whether you sanitize or not, the responsibility for death is not a weight we should flippantly toss onto another human's shoulders, especially one who is honestly trying to do what they think is right. Even if it's different from what you think is right.

This is easier to understand when you have fought someone else's death and lost. When you have tried to save a patient and failed, when you have lain awake at night wondering if one more thing or one different procedure or one minute better spent might have saved a life that you lost. *You. Lost.* As if the preservation of all human life (even that which is 99.9% eked out by the time you arrive on scene) is your burden to bear.

When you have lost a life you tried to save, you understand that death is not something to be casually thrown in the face of your neighbor with whom you disagree.

COVID isn't the only threat in this world. Each step, each choice, carries its own small dangers, its own potential risks.

Every time you get into a car, every morning you allow your child to get out of bed. Every toy you buy, every bite of solid food you take, every tree you climb, every stair you go down, every concert you attend, every time you have sex. Every school you enter, plane you board, bike you ride. Every fitness class or walk in the sun, every swim at the beach or taste of smoked meat. Every exercise you do. Every exercise you don't do. Every roller coaster. Every hand you hold, every lip you kiss.

Every morning you get up is a morning you could die.

Every morning you get up is a morning you could accidentally kill someone else.

Would you take the mornings away? The sun, the food, the beaches, the swims, the movement, the lovemaking, the hugs, the cars, the cell phones, the birthday cakes, the hard candies, the hard laughter, the aches, the aging, the mistakes, the successes? Would you weight every moment, every thought, with the potential death you could suffer or cause to another?

To do so is to rob yourself of life.

To do so is to carry or give a burden that can't be held without crushing the holder.

Which isn't to say that in living, we have to live recklessly. Which isn't to say we don't buy bike helmets and car seats, don't apply sunscreen or wear condoms, don't eat vegetables or wear Fitbits. Which isn't to say that in the midst of a new disease it might be prudent to wear a mask or scrub our hands extra clean.

Which is only to say that life cannot escape death. Which is only to say we shouldn't casually cast that responsibility upon our neighbors, or even ourselves.

Most days we save lives.

But some days we lose them.

Hold it. Own it. Make peace with it.

Or you will find yourself living a hundred years without ever knowing a single day, a casualty to your own fear or hate or perfect righteousness. Lost to the life you could hold—you do hold—so preciously in your own hands.

Because They Were Falling

I see dead people—not because I was born with a paranormal ability to see spirits and help them resolve old issues—but because in my work as a paramedic there are a surprising number to see. The dead, the old, the infirm, the panicked, and the truly stricken. Sometimes they march along in quick succession. Sometimes we have long pauses in between.

It's an interesting choice of work, one where you walk into the houses of strangers and pick them up off the ground—sometimes literally, sometimes figuratively. I see people at their lowest moments, in puddles of excrement or blood, in arguments so bad that the police have been called, and in times of loss so unexpected that family members stand in shock and mourning discussing funeral arrangements when just that morning they were chatting about á trip to the grocery store.

And, whether the call is truly emergent or not, whether wounds (inside and outside the body) are self-inflicted or not, whether people have dug themselves into holes so deep it's more than a trip to the ER could ever fix, we show up. We bring in our equipment. We pick people up.

It's the hardest part of my job, picking people up.

Sometimes I don't want to do it because I know that I'll just be there again the next night and the next, that no matter how many times I pick them up, they'll fall again, no matter how many rides to the hospital to fix a phantom illness, they'll always have another. Or sometimes I know that I can no longer pick them up because they won't be coming back, not in this life anyway, and I have to tell people that. Even as we hook the dead body up to our equipment just to be sure that there's no way, no possible way, to bring them back.

So why do we do it, call after call, life after life? Why do we pick people up when we know we'll find them on the ground again? Or worse, we won't—because they are gone.

Some people say that it's because of that one—the one we save, the little child we cut out of a car, the woman who wakes up the next day because we fixed her sugar in time, the person we resuscitate whose breath and heart return to normal. And *the one* is important. Those are beautiful calls, days that make me fly instead of crawl, days that people create movies out of because they're so wonderful, so extraordinary, so inspiring that crowds will pay to watch the story. But the one, as great as it is, could never keep me going. The high could never hold long enough. Too many bodies in between, dead and alive.

Still I come back to those bodies. Sit them up when I can, explain to a family when I cannot. And why?

I grew up in the mountain west, where it snowed a lot in winter. That first snow was always treacherous. During summer, while we were all practicing our speed tricks and road rage, everyone forgot how to drive in the winter weather. And then that first sheet of white hit, thick and slick. People slid off the road by the literal dozens that first day, every year. And the most amazing thing happened. Instead of honking and cursing at that idiot in front of us, we would get out of our cars—total strangers—to dig or push them out. It happened a lot. People forgot their differences, broke through their prejudices and politics, and pushed their neighbor back onto the road.

It doesn't just happen in the snow. It happens in car accidents, in floods, tornadoes, hurricanes. It happens when a woman goes into labor. It happens when a person faints at an event. It happens during heart attacks and on playgrounds.

Several years ago, we got called to a fire—four pediatric patients inside a burning house. We were the first on scene, arriving even before the firefighters. But *we* didn't rescue those kids. They were brought to us by family and neighbors. As soon as we arrived, a person rushed up carrying a little girl, maybe seven years old, who was unresponsive. I took her into the ambulance and prepared to intubate as someone else shouted, "There's more." Bad news since I was the only paramedic on scene at the time.

"Are they crying?" I asked. They were, which was good. It meant they were alert with an airway. It didn't mean their burns weren't bad. It didn't mean they didn't need care. But it meant they could wait a little longer in the arms of other people while I took care of the girl. One of the neighbors stayed in the ambulance, helping me with the three children who were now under my care. He provided desperately needed support as I tended to the girl's airway. It worked. The girl began to breathe, and then cry. The best sound in all the world when it's a scene with children.

Other crews arrived, and we got a handle on the situation, all with the help of a crowd of people who weren't on the clock, who weren't helping so they could get a paycheck or a movie contract or a date with a girl. Just people, there in the middle of the night, working in potentially dangerous circumstances for free.

This happens enough that, even when it doesn't, even when you show up at a lonely trailer to pick an old lady up because she fell down (again), even when an addict is running around Sonic butt naked (again), even when you get the domestic call (sadly, again), you can remember—the times when the neighbors came together, the times when the strangers gathered around an accident, the times regular people carried children from a fire.

Superman catches people just because they fall. If you asked him why, he probably wouldn't say, "Because they deserved it," or "Because they were beautiful," or "Because they were little and I knew it wouldn't hurt my arms." No. I think if we asked Superman why he catches people, he would say, "Because they were falling."

I'm not Superman, and neither—probably—are you. But when people fall, we try to catch them. It's why you help push a guy out of the snow; it's why you muck mud out of a neighbor's basement after a flash flood; it's why you hold a crying baby if the mother cannot.

It's why I show up for work.

It's why I'm grateful for all the other people who do too.

We show up because people fall. Because we all fall. And so, we catch.

Acknowledgments

In both writing and life (and this book encompasses a good bit of both), there are always a bunch of people to thank. We're going to give it our best shot.

A huge thank you to Officers Kyle, Jake, and Brittni. Thank you for your insights on how the law enforcement side of everything works so we don't sound like idiots (hopefully) when talking about the cops. If we do sound like idiots, let it be known that it's our own fault and not theirs.

We have the lovely and talented Shillawna Ruffner to thank for the photograph of James that is featured on the cover (and taken in the middle of an ice storm).

A big shout out to our beta readers: Rebecca, Sarah, Michelle, and Naomi. Your insights helped give this thing shape, and kept it from being only sad stories. And after all that reworking, thank you to our final editor, Carrie, for making the manuscript sparkle.

James would like to thank his ER family—the nurses, doctors, office staff, EMTs, and other medics. Maybe the years of parking lot Olympics and triathlons are over, but they can't take the memories away.

Throughout the years, James has had a lot of partners (not to mention the pilots, flight crew, police officers, and firefighters) who have participated on calls—calls that can be heartbreaking, bizarre, hilarious, or inane. You guys do so much unsung work (still unsung since most of your names have been removed from this in order to protect your privacy), and have helped keep James sane throughout the years. Thank you. We'd like to give a special acknowledgment to Brad who, besides being a fantastic paramedic and friend, helped jog James' memory about some of the crazy and funny things that have happened over the years.

We'd both like to thank our families. You guys support us and believe in us. You'll probably even buy this book (although we'd give you one for free; we promise). Some of you will buy multiple copies. Just because you're awesome.

And last of all, a thank you to our children—for being them, for living in a life with weird EMS schedules (all those early and late Christmases), for going with the flow, for giving love, for all the things you do just because you're you. You guys are the pulse of our family.

Also by J.K. Pace

If you enjoyed this, you might also enjoy *Four Seconds*, a real life story of addiction and recovery, written by Jean Knight Pace and Laura Andrade.

In her debut memoir, Laura Andrade tells of her years with cocaine and crystal methamphetamines—using, then selling—until all she had left of the life she wanted was a chalk outline and a pack of cigarettes. This is the story of her use and recovery, of the people who frustrated and inspired her, of her decision to leave the drug world. It is the story of her slow, often unsteady walk home.

If you enjoy fiction, you might also enjoy Jean's women's fiction (under the name J.E. Pace), featuring hometown heroes: a firefighter, a paramedic, and an accidental police detective.

You can get a **free copy of the first story, "Ready," by signing up for the newsletter HERE.** In the newsletter, you'll get also get exclusive deals and be the first to hear about sales or live events.

Or you can just jump into the **full-length novel, *From Ashes*.** (Not sure fiction is for you? You can find the prologue at the end of this book in the Bonus section.)

If that's not fun enough, you can find me at jeanknightpace.com where, in addition to all the bookish news, I include random thoughts and pictures of animals.

About the Authors

James Pace has worked in EMS for twenty-three years—three as an EMT and twenty as a paramedic, with a few years on the helicopter thrown in for good measure. When he's not out saving lives (or lift assisting people), he enjoys racquetball, animals, and movies with big heroes. He's the father of four and husband to one.

J.K. PACE IS the author of *From Ashes* (under the name J.E. Pace). Her other works include *Hugging Death: Essays on Motherhood and Saying Goodbye* as well as *Four Seconds* (written with Laura Andrade). She has had essays and short stories published in *Puerto del Sol, The Lakeview Review,* and other literary magazines. She lives in Indiana with her husband, four children, eight ducks, four chickens, and a cat. You can find more about her at jeanknightpace.com.

Facebook
Instagram
Amazon

Goodreads
TikTok

Bonus!

PROLOGUE FOR FROM ASHES (A FICTIONAL FIREFIGHTER NOVEL AVAILABLE ON AMAZON)

She showed up at half past three. That's a.m. in case anyone was wondering. Rang the bell. A shocking sound at that time in the morning, no matter how long I'd been doing this job, no matter how accustomed I was to the middle-of-the night tones, the sirens long and shrill. Still that doorbell startled me. I jerked out of bed, threw on my pants and stumbled into the main room, fuzzy brained. It rang again.

People come to the fire station sometimes, bringing their emergencies to us, instead of calling 911 for us to go to them. A wreck just outside the station, a man with a bloody forehead from the bar a mile away. And every once in a while—though never in the middle of the night—a homeschool group asking for a tour, or a sweet old lady with a cheesecake or pie, thanking us for the things we do.

But not tonight. Tonight I released the lock, opened the door. Tonight a woman stumbled in, old car seat dangling from a scarred arm. Sweats and torn tank top. Ball cap covering her face. Not that I could have seen her anyway. She looked down the whole time. I couldn't have told you

168

what color her eyes were even if I'd tried. Her cheeks were pocked though. Scars from picking. Lips chapped. Both forearms lined with old needle scars, though I didn't see anything new at first glance.

Baby set on the floor. Six words. "I can't take care of her."

And the woman was gone, though for a moment her scent lingered, old blood and body odor and something sour from the night.

I peered into the second-hand car seat that sat on the floor. A little thing squirmed inside. We hadn't had a surrender for a long time—almost ten months.

I lifted the baby out of the seat—she wasn't even buckled in. I moved the blanket down a notch so I could see her face. The baby opened its mouth—her mouth; the woman had called the baby a girl—and squinched her eyes. I bounced her a second, but still the cry came. Solid. Committed. You had to respect a cry like that.

The engineer, Jessie, came in, suspenders dangling down around her waist, and set a cup of coffee down on the counter. "Been a while." That's all she said, peeking over the pink-gray blanket.

A bruise ran up the baby's forehead in a purple line. Jessie and I looked at each other.

"Did you give the mother your spiel, 'You're doing a brave thing for your baby' and yada yada all that?"

"Nah, I didn't have time. She didn't exactly stay for tea."

"They never do," Jessie said.

They never do.

"She probably didn't deserve your comfort speech anyway," Jessie said, taking a swig of her coffee. "Better get the baby to the ER so they can check her out before handing the kid over to child protective services."

"It really is a brave thing to do for the babies," I say.

"It's the *best* thing," Jessie replied. "That's for sure. Don't know if I can get behind the word *brave*."

She called dispatch to have them page out the EMS unit to pick up a surrender. I bundled the baby up tight.

"You've got a knack," Jessie said, then looked away like she realized her mistake.

My wife and I had been trying. Over two years now. Calendars first, timers, then the drugs. Next step, in vitro, but neither of us was sure we were ready for that. In fact, we were pretty sure we weren't.

My bouncing had turned to a soft rock, then a full on swing. The wailing stopped. Face relaxed, eyes open.

Green as the sea.

Made in the USA
Monee, IL
13 December 2024

73551707R00104